ERNST HEIDEMANN, L'EUROPEO, ITALY

"Excuse me! I didn't see you coming."

DUBOUT, LE RIRE, FRANCE

CARTOON TREASURY

CARTOON TREASURY

PEN AND PENCIL HUMOR OF THE WORLD

Edited by LUCY BLACK JOHNSON AND PYKE JOHNSON, JR.

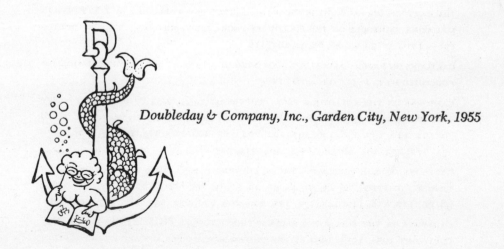

Doubleday & Company, Inc., Garden City, New York, 1955

for Lucy Grey Stimson and Pyke Johnson

THE CARTOON ON PAGE 283 IS FROM *Our Little Nuns*, PUBLISHED BY EXTENSION MAGAZINE. CARTOONS ON THE FOLLOWING PAGES, COPYRIGHT 1953, 1954 BY HULTON PRESS, LTD., 37, 39, 42, 46, 88, 94, 107, 118

CARTOONS ON PAGE 281 FROM THE BOOK *Statues*, COPYRIGHT 1954 BY GEORGE MOLNAR. PUBLISHED BY E. P. DUTTON & CO., INC.

CARTOONS ON THE FOLLOWING PAGES, COPYRIGHT 1953, 1954 BY BRADBURY, AGNEW & COMPANY, LTD., PROPRIETORS OF PUNCH: 16, 23, 25, 34, 38, 61, 63, 72, 73, 74, 78, 79, 101, 126, 137, 138, 146, 147, 182, 204, 205, 209, 210, 225, 231, 254, 264, 270, 271, 272, 275, 284, 287, 293, 295, 304, 311, 315

CARTOONS ON THE FOLLOWING PAGES, COPYRIGHT 1953, 1954 BY THE CURTIS PUBLISHING COMPANY: 12, 23, 30, 44, 45, 49, 57, 64, 65, 68, 73, 81, 82, 83, 85, 87, 94, 98, 99, 117, 118, 140, 145, 174, 175, 200, 209, 240, 252, 257, 276, 287, 294

CARTOONS ON THE FOLLOWING PAGES REPRINTED FROM THIS WEEK MAGAZINE, COPYRIGHT 1952, 1953, 1954 BY THE UNITED NEWSPAPERS MAGAZINE CORPORATION: 45, 96, 145, 150, 154, 170, 197, 241

EDITORS' NOTE

In assembling this volume of humorous cartoons the editors have looked at thousands of drawings from all parts of the world, but in making the final selection they have been guided by one consideration only: Is it funny? Although this is certainly the most comprehensive collection of international cartoons ever brought into one volume, the arrangement is deliberately non-national. Students who wish to draw profound conclusions concerning the differences in national humor of, say, the Americans and the British, the French and the Germans, the Brazilians and the Italians, will find the material here, but they will receive no help from the editors in digging it out.

One branch of the cartoon field—the American comic strip—is missing from this book. The editors shut the door reluctantly to Pogo, Peanuts, Fan Fare, Li'l Abner, the Lichty panels, and others. But part of the success of these drawings depends upon their continuity and a familiarity with them, and we did not feel we could represent them adequately in the space available. We found consolation for this decision in the fact that the best of the comic strips have already appeared in book form.

The vast majority of the cartoons in this volume have never before appeared in book form. There were a few cartoons we wished to include which were not available to us. Aside from this handful, the book achieves what we set out to do at the beginning: to bring the funniest cartoons of the current crop into one big handsome volume, a volume to whose reader it can be truly said, "Laugh, and the world laughs with you."

The idea for CARTOON TREASURY originated with the Doubleday trade department, and in a very real sense this has been "a Doubleday book." The list of those who have contributed to its making is too long to be printed here. The editors must therefore content themselves with making a general acknowledgment to the many persons (both in and out of Doubleday) whose encouragement and assistance have done more than anything else to make this book possible.

Particular thanks, of course, must be given to the artists and the editors who have granted permission for the use of their drawings in this volume. Some of them have other cartoons in books or anthologies of their own. It is our hope that the taste given here will stimulate the reader to look at these books:

A Century of Punch Cartoons, published by Simon & Schuster

George Molnar's *Statues*, published by E. P. Dutton

What's Funny About That? A Cartoon Carnival from This Week Magazine, published by E. P. Dutton

Honey, I'm Home: Cartoons from the Saturday Evening Post, published by E. P. Dutton

James Simpkins' *Jasper*, published by the Ryerson Press, Toronto

The Tattooed Sailor, by André François, published by Alfred A. Knopf

The Female Approach, by Ronald Searle, published by Alfred A. Knopf

The editors wish to acknowledge help in obtaining material given by the staffs of Doubleday's overseas offices: Deirdre Butler and St. Clair Pugh in Paris and Barbara Noble and Violet Barton in London. We are also indebted to Harold Strauss who interrupted a trip to Japan to assist us, to Fred Rosenau who brought us much material from South America, and to John Barkham who put us in touch with his friends in many parts of the world. We are grateful for the work done in obtaining permissions by Douglas McKee in France and Ole Branner in Denmark.

For advice and assistance we are grateful to William Cole, editor of several anthologies of his own, who freely shared his experience and material with us.

Of the many in Doubleday's New York office who worked on this book, we wish to make special acknowledgment to four persons:

To Walter Bradbury, our editor, neighbor, and friend, for helping to smooth out more than one spot.

To Diana Klemin, who contributed the skill and imagination necessary to make a book out of a collection of drawings and clippings.

To Ursula Smith, who gave invaluable assistance with correspondence and with German translations.

And to Mrs. Christine Pollard of the Permissions Department (unsung heroes of any publishing house), who spent long hours at night and over weekends handling the onerous and vital chore of permissions.

It is no exaggeration to say that the best parts of this book are the results of the work of those mentioned here.

Lucy Black Johnson
Pyke Johnson, Jr.

Riverside, Connecticut

CARTOON TREASURY

LORIOT, WELTBILD, GERMANY

LIQUORS

CHON DAY, TRUE, U.S.

SPOHR, NEUE ILLUSTRIERTE, GERMANY

8

FEYER, MACLEAN'S, CANADA

RONALD SEARLE, ENGLAND

"Quick! To the station!"

ISIDORI, IL TRAVASO, ITALY

TETSU, FRANCE DIMANCHE, FRANCE

"Stick 'em up!"
CHAVAL, PARIS-MATCH, FRANCE

"I was here first!"
BELLI, IL TRAVASO, ITALY

10

"I don't know what he sees in her!"
LU KRENCZEK, LUSTIGE ILLUSTRIERTE, GERMANY

TON SMITS, MEDICAL ECONOMICS, U. S.

"I'll never forgive you for that 'bravo' when the tenor fell into the orchestra pit."

CHON DAY, THE SATURDAY EVENING POST, U.S.

12

1

2

CHAVAL, PARIS-MATCH, FRANCE

LEON, DER STERN, GERMANY

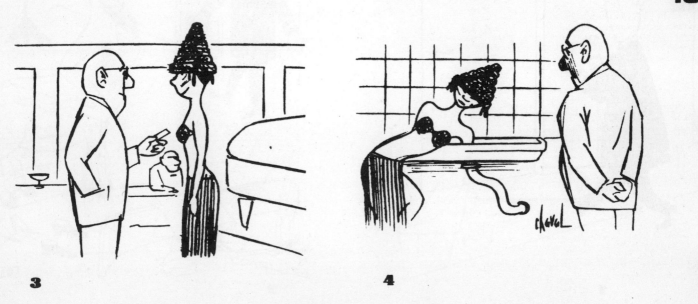

3

4

COSPER, HUDIBRAS, DENMARK

LOTHAR URSINUS, GERMANY

CUSTOMS

15

"There's a car like ours."

CHAVAL, PARIS-MATCH, FRANCE

SIGGS, © PUNCH, ENGLAND

16

SEMPÉ, SAMEDI-SOIR, FRANCE

FINAL RESULTS

ROLAND, MANCHETE, BRAZIL

"Juliet, I'm beginning to think you no longer love me."

BORTOLATO, L'EUROPEO, ITALY

18

GANTRIIS, HUDIBRAS, DENMARK

MICHEL DOUAY, PARIS-MATCH, FRANCE

"It's that man from the telephone office."

JOHN FRAZER, THE TEXAS RANGER, U. S.

19

ANDRÉ FRANÇOIS, FRANCE

SEMPÉ, ICI PARIS, FRANCE

20

"*Anyone in?*"

NORMAN HETHERINGTON, THE SYDNEY BULLETIN, AUSTRALIA

HANS FISCHER, DER STERN, GERMANY

"*Now, let's make a target out of this.*"

HERB WILLIAMS, COLLIER'S, U.S.

BOSC, PARIS-MATCH, FRANCE

ISIDORI, IL TRAVASO, ITALY

22

ENVY

CONSIGLI, IL TRAVASO, ITALY

"Open your mouth and shut your eyes, darling."

NÉO, LE RIRE, FRANCE

MICHEL DOUAY, FRANCE DIMANCHE, FRANCE

HANS FISCHER, DER STERN, GERMANY

"Come in, come in! It's good to see you folks again!"

BEN THOMPSON, THE SATURDAY EVENING POST, U. S.

23

JÜRG SPAHR, DIE WOCHE, SWITZERLAND

24   JEAN DEJOUX, PARIS-MATCH, FRANCE

TREZ, SAMEDI-SOIR, FRANCE

"All right, Brannigan—we know you're in there!"

J. W. TAYLOR, © PUNCH, ENGLAND

25

"Of course, this is one of my very earliest."

RONALD SEARLE, ENGLAND

NASLUND, SE, SWEDEN

BOSC, SAMEDI-SOIR, FRANCE

27

DETERMINATION OF THE BRITISH TO ENSURE THAT THEIR SONS INHERIT THEIR TRADITIONAL LOVE OF THE SEA.

GILES, LONDON DAILY EXPRESS, ENGLAND

"Hey, dim your lights!"

ERNST HEIDEMANN, DER STERN, GERMANY

28

THE EIGHT AGES OF WOMANHOOD

"SHE'S SEVEN—she simply won't do what she's told."

"SHE'S 17—she's always in tears over some man."

"Quick, undress, here comes my wife!"
FRANZ FÜCHSEL, DENMARK

BOSC, PARIS-MATCH, FRANCE

"SHE'S 27—she thinks she's a fund of experience."

"SHE'S 37—she talks of nothing but the children."

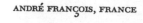

"Say when."

STARKE, THE SATURDAY EVENING POST, U. S.

ANDRÉ FRANÇOIS, FRANCE

"SHE'S 47 — she simply won't grow old gracefully."

SHE'S 57—she insists she's lonely and unwanted."

"Get my WHAT out of your bar?"

BILL YATES, TRUE, U.S.

"SHE'S 77—she growls at our guests."

"SHE'S 87—she simply won't do what she's told"

GILES, LONDON DAILY EXPRESS, ENGLAND

"Well, do you want it with shoulder straps or without?"

GANTRIIS, HUDIBRAS, DENMARK

tetsu

TSU, SAMEDI-SOIR, FRANCE

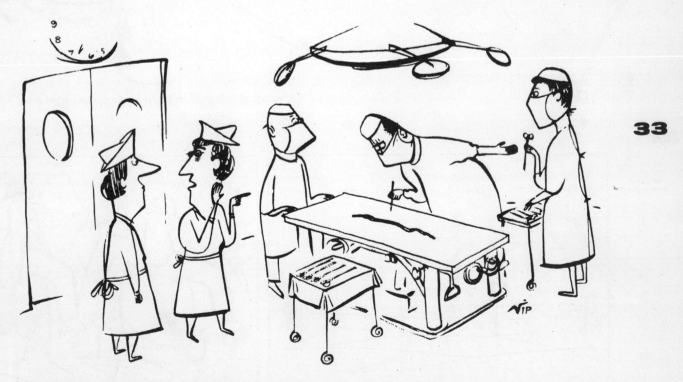

33

"Dr. Colmore is operating on a shoestring."

VIRGIL PARTCH, COLLIER'S, U. S.

THELWELL, © PUNCH, ENGLAND

"Quit that stirring. Don't you know what night it is?"

SIMPKINS, MACLEAN'S, CANADA

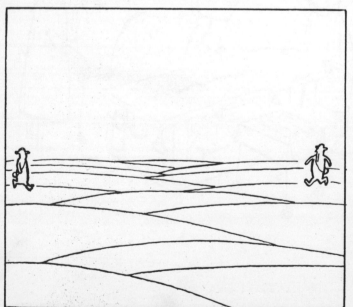

MOROSETTI, IL TRAVASO, ITALY

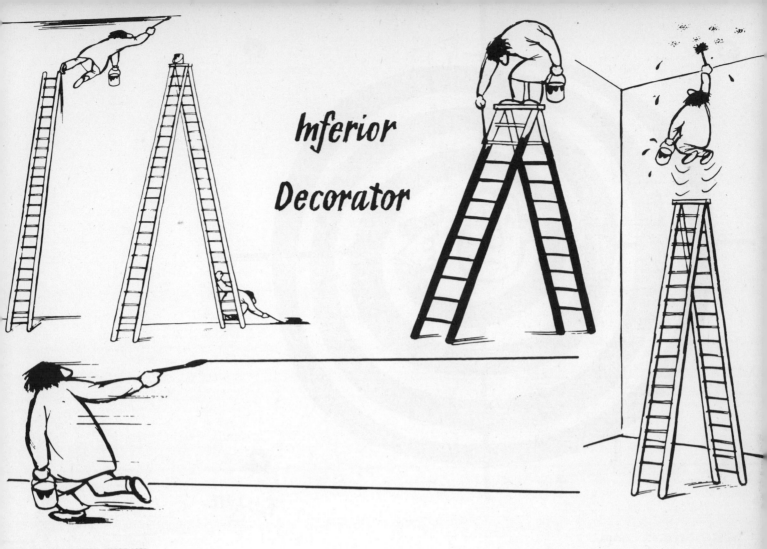

Inferior
Decorator

35

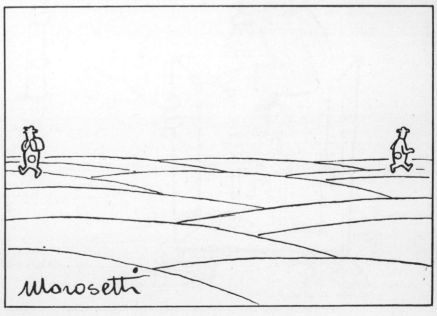

Morosetti

36

BORTOLATO, SETTIMO GIORNO, ITALY

"... *or forever hold his peace* ..."

STARKE, LILLIPUT, ENGLAND

FEYER, MACLEAN'S, CANADA

DAVID MORROW, © PUNCH, ENGLAND

FEYER, MACLEAN'S, CANADA

38

FEYER, MACLEAN'S, CANADA

CONSIGLI, IL TRAVASO, ITALY

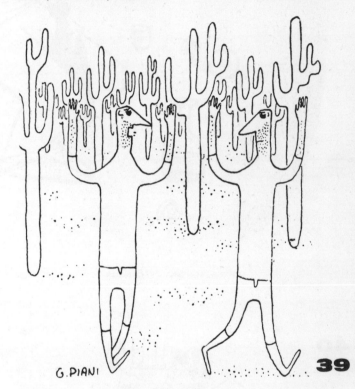

39

"Cactus, cactus everywhere! It's becoming an obsession!"

Feyer

FEYER, MACLEAN'S, CANADA

40

SILENCE

KANT

WOLTER-

"Haven't you something a little lighter?"

WOLTER, LUSTIGE ILLUSTRIERTE, GERMANY

"Pepsi Cola hits the spot. Pepsi Cola hits the spot. Pepsi Cola . . ."

AMI, NOIR ET BLANC, FRANCE

"It's for you."

RODRIGUES, MACLEAN'S, CANADA

"Now *what is he saying?*"

TONY BARLOW, COLLIER'S, U. S.

CUP FINAL

RAY, MEN ONLY AND LONDON OPINION, ENGLAND

41

TETSU, LE RIRE, FRANCE

ERIC BURGIN, LILLIPUT, ENGLAND

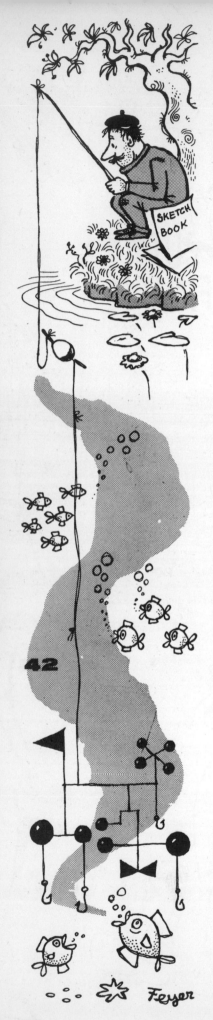

FEYER, MACLEAN'S, CANADA

AMI, LILLIPUT, ENGLAND

"Mama's sorry. Mama didn't realize that you wanted one that goes squeak when you press its tummy."

FOG, MACLEAN'S, CANADA

BORTOLATO, LE ORE, ITALY

44

"Why don't you hang out the window like other dogs?"

GALLAGHER, THE SATURDAY EVENING POST, U. S.

"I said, 'Boooooooooo.'"

GUY BARA, ICI PARIS, FRANCE

Feyer

FEYER, MACLEAN'S, CANADA

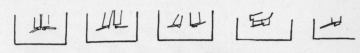

"Do you have something with a smaller check?"

DRUCKER, THE SATURDAY EVENING POST, U. S.

45

"Wait until you see where I mounted my new Hi-Fi speaker."

LUNDBERG, THIS WEEK, U. S.

"My God! They're returning our fire!"

BORTOLATO, LE ORE, ITALY

ANTON, LILLIPUT, ENGLAND

TOM JOHNSON, STANFORD CHAPARRAL, U. S.

"Hurry up! We haven't got all day!"

BORTOLATO, EPOCA, ITALY

"It was great, Mom! The pilot came out and talked to us after Pop pinched the hostess."

IRWIN CAPLAN, COLLIER'S, U. S.

"Are you sure your mistress ordered 30,000 leftover bones?"

SILVA, CALIFORNIA PELICAN, U. S.

WILLIAM O'BRIAN, ARGOSY, U. S.

48

AMI, LILLIPUT, ENGLAND

LEON, DER STERN, GERMANY

COSTUMES FOR RENT

JOSEPH ZEIS, THE SATURDAY EVENING POST, U. S.

OSKAR METTE, DER STERN, GERMANY

SMILBY, LONDON OPINION, ENGLAND

"It isn't much, but it's home."

VIRGIL PARTCH, COLLIER'S, U. S.

50

WOLTER, LUSTIGE ILLUSTRIERTE, GERMANY

GUY BARA, SAMEDI-SOIR, FRANCE

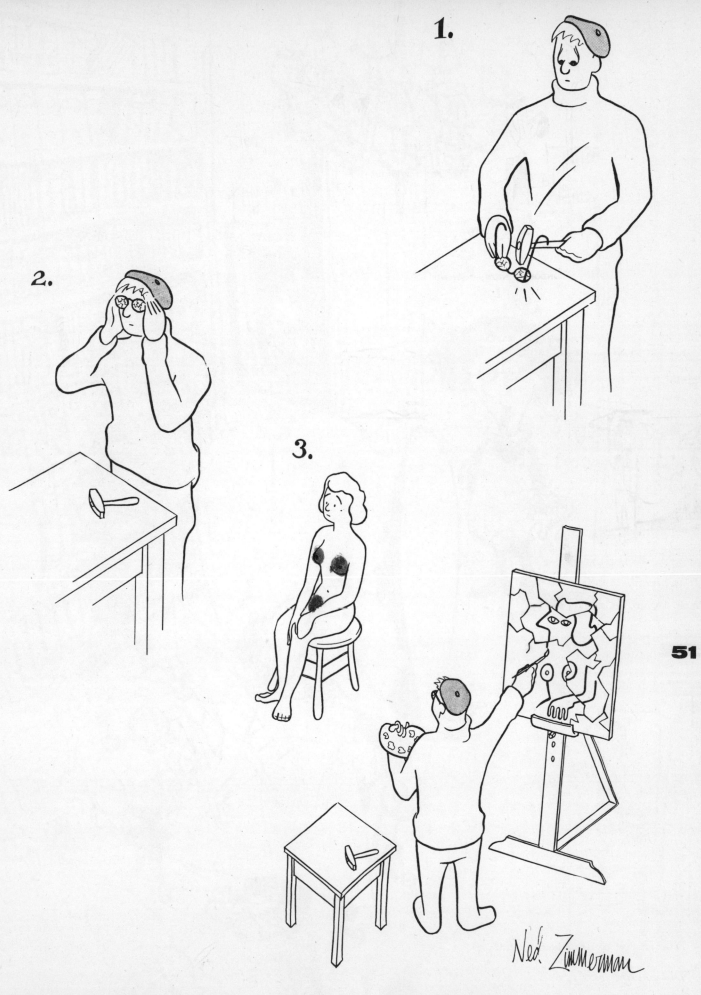

1.

2.

3.

51

52

"Did you ring, Sir?"

HOFFNUNG, LILLIPUT, ENGLAND

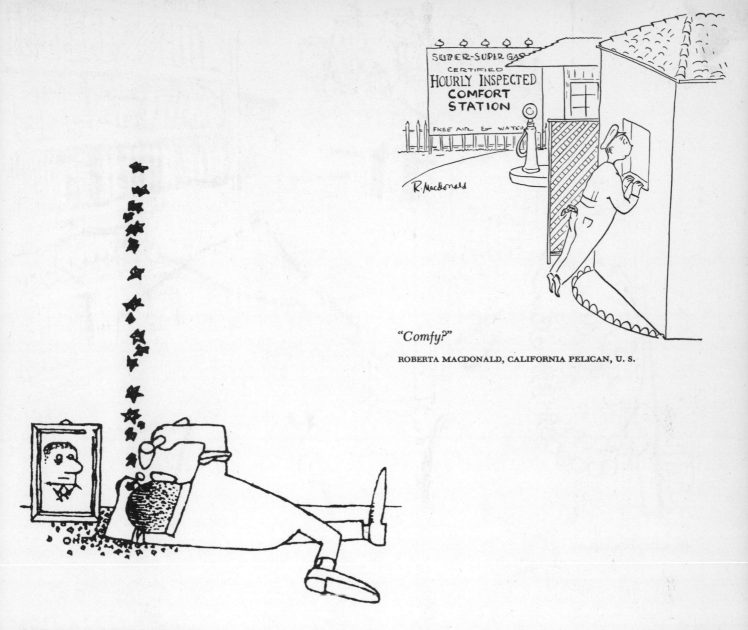

"Comfy?"

ROBERTA MACDONALD, CALIFORNIA PELICAN, U. S.

SPOHR, NEUE ILLUSTRIERTE, GERMANY

THELWELL, MEN ONLY AND LONDON OPINION, ENGLAND

AL KAUFMAN, MACLEAN'S, CANADA

FOG, MACLEAN'S, CANADA

FEYER, MACLEAN'S, CANADA

"My landlady's daughter was my model and I could have tripled my output
if she had bathed more than once a week."

WOLTER, LUSTIGE ILLUSTRIERTE, GERMANY

HOFFNUNG, LILLIPUT, ENGLAND

56

"Hello, you fatheaded moron!"

BILL HARRISON, SUCCESSFUL FARMING, U. S.

LEON, DER STERN, GERMANY

"*I just slipped them off for a minute to ease my feet.*"

THELWELL, LONDON OPINION, ENGLAND

57

ROWLAND WILSON, THE SATURDAY EVENING POST, U. S.

58

DAVID LANGDON, MACLEAN'S, CANADA

"Would you mind removing your halo?"

JACK MAXWELL, IL TRAVASO, ITALY

A. HARVEC, FRANCE DIMANCHE, FRANCE

"Signora Bettoni? I don't know her. I'm new here."

MOROSETTI, L'EUROPEO, ITALY

LEON, DER STERN, GERMANY

"What kind of bait are you using?"

BORTOLATO, L'EUROPEO, ITALY

60

BORTOLATO, LE ORE, ITALY

"...left—right—left—right—left—right..."

SPOHR, DER STERN, GERMANY

FFOLKES, © PUNCH, ENGLAND

BORTOLATO, L'EUROPEO, ITALY

61

MICHEL DOUAY, CARREFOUR, FRANCE

GUY BARA, SAMEDI-SOIR, FRANCE

SPOHR, DER STERN, GERMANY

62

"What's so unusual about a one-piece bathing suit?"

BILL HARRISON, ARGOSY, U. S.

FEYER, MACLEAN'S, CANADA

VENNER WITTING, © PUNCH, ENGLAND

63

MARKUS, DER STERN, GERMANY

"I don't like it!"

HARRY MACE, THE SATURDAY EVENING POST, U. S.

64

"I knocked and knocked—then decided to try the back door."

LAMB, SAGA, U. S.

FEYER, MACLEAN'S, CANADA

"...told you we should have brought the children ..."

ENGLISH, MACLEAN'S, CANADA

THE PLAGIARIST

WOLTER, LUSTIGE ILLUSTRIERTE, GERMANY

"Sam!"

65

SHIRVANIAN, THE SATURDAY EVENING POST, U. S.

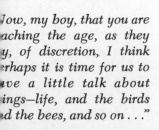

"...Now, my boy, that you are reaching the age, as they say, of discretion, I think perhaps it is time for us to have a little talk about things—life, and the birds and the bees, and so on ..."

HOFFNUNG, LILLIPUT, ENGLAND

1

2

3

JACK MAXWELL, IL TRAVASO, ITALY

66

4 5 6 7

JÜRG SPAHR, DIE WOCHE, SWITZERLAND

"He's an ex-convict."

CONSIGLI, IL TRAVASO, ITALY

SIM, SAMEDI-SOIR, FRANCE

9

10

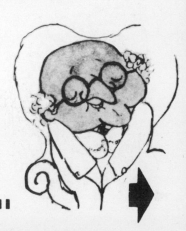

11

"Hello, sugar."

TON SMITS, COLLIER'S, U. S.

"Just a moment, old man ..."

GALLAGHER, THE SATURDAY EVENING POST, U. S.

68

"Hello, darling, I'm home."

MARKUS, DER STERN, GERMANY

"You could at least lift your feet."

A. HARVEC, LA PRESSE, FRANCE

12

13

14

15

ELIE

ELIE, ICI PARIS, FRANCE

"Can I keep him? He followed me home from school."

RAY HELLE, BETTER HOMES & GARDENS, U.S.

17

69

PETER WYMA, MACLEAN'S, CANADA

Peter Wyma

FEYER, MACLEAN'S, CANADA

FISCHER, NEUE ILLUSTRIERTE, GERMANY

70

GOBI, ESQUIRE, U. S.

FEYER, MACLEAN'S, CANADA

"He did it!"

BORTOLATO, SETTIMO GIORNO, ITALY

"Just a little further back ..."

ETSU, NOIR ET BLANC, FRANCE

71

72 *"Let's have it a bit more rampant, George."*

WOOLCOCK, LONDON OPINION, ENGLAND

CONSIGLI, IL TRAVASO, ITALY

ADAMSON, © PUNCH, ENGLAND

"She loves me, she loves me not, she loves me ..."

BORTOLATO, SETTIMO GIORNO, ITALY

AMI, FRANCE DIMANCHE, FRANCE

"Whatever your mother says goes, and I think you'll find she'll bear me out on that."

LEPPER, THE SATURDAY EVENING POST, U. S.

73

FFOLKES, © PUNCH, ENGLAND

74

FEYER, MACLEAN'S, CANADA

TON SMITS, COLLIER'S, U. S.

TETSU, NOIR ET BLANC, FRANCE

75

76

J. MAXWELL

THE STOWAWAY

JACK MAXWELL, FORCES AERIENNES FRANCAISES, FRANCE

AMI, FRANCE DIMANCHE, FRANCE

RAY, LONDON OPINION, ENGLAND

77

AL KAUFMAN, MACLEAN'S, CANADA

"Look, chief . . . Bell-bottom pants!"

VIRGIL PARTCH, COLLIER'S, U. S.

MOFREY, SAMEDI-SOIR, FRANCE

78

"How much is this one?"

WILLIAM SCULLY, © PUNCH, ENGLAND

G. PIANI, IL TRAVASO, ITALY

PERSONNEL (SALARIES)

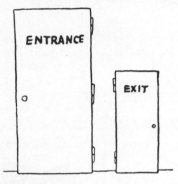

LIMMROTH, QUICK, GERMANY

BERTHAU, DER STERN, GERMANY

79

"Grow, d'you hear!! . . . Grow!!!"

GRAHAM, © PUNCH, ENGLAND

SIM, LE HERISSON, FRANCE

80

JÜRG SPAHR, DIE WOCHE, SWITZERLAND

"So I said, 'Emma Kimball'—that was close—I said, 'you take back every word you said about ...'"

JERRY MARCUS, THE SATURDAY EVENING POST, U. S.

BILL RUBLE, SUCCESSFUL FARMING, U. S.

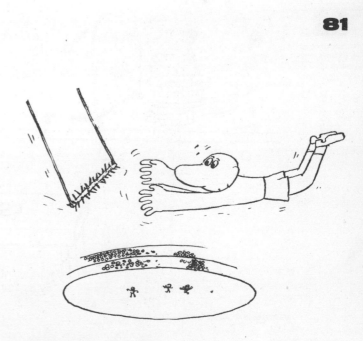

CONSIGLI, IL TRAVASO, ITALY

MOROSETTI, GIORNALE D'ITALIA DELLA DOMENICA, ITALY

82

BERNHARDT, BETTER FARMING, U. S.

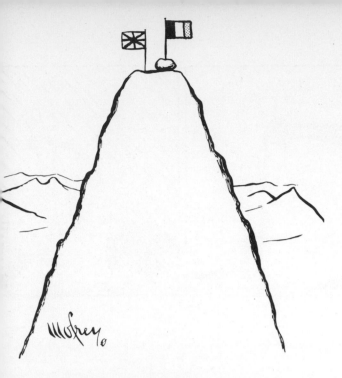

MOFREY, FRANCE DIMANCHE, FRANCE

RENÉ CHAG, SAMEDI-SOIR, FRANCE

SMILBY, LONDON OPINION, ENGLAND

"Say when!"

TON SMITS, COLLIER'S, U. S.

SYVERSON, THE SATURDAY EVENING POST, U. S.

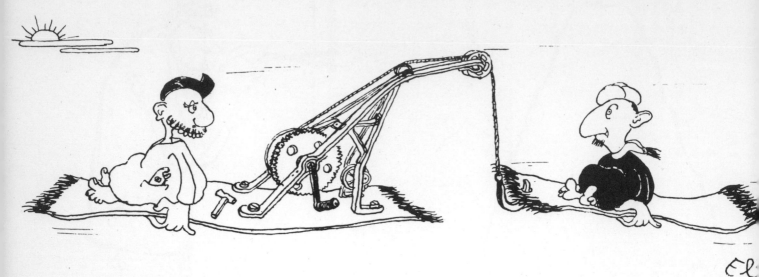

ELZI, DIE WOCHE, SWITZERLAND

84

JÜRG SPAHR, MONSIEUR, SWITZERLAND

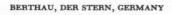

bert

BERTHAU, DER STERN, GERMANY

CON SUOZZI

CON SUOZZI, BETTER FARMING, U. S.

85

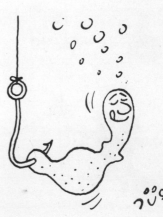

JÜRG SPAHR, MONSIEUR, SWITZERLAND

86

AL KAUFMAN, MACLEAN'S, CANADA

SELF-PORTRAIT

CONSIGLI, IL TRAVASO, ITALY

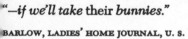
"—*if we'll take their bunnies.*"

BARLOW, LADIES' HOME JOURNAL, U. S.

RENÉ CHAG, SAMEDI-SOIR, FRANCE

JUST
MARRIED

JACK MAXWELL, ITALY

"*I told you he would be furious!*"

BORTOLATO, LE ORO, ITALY

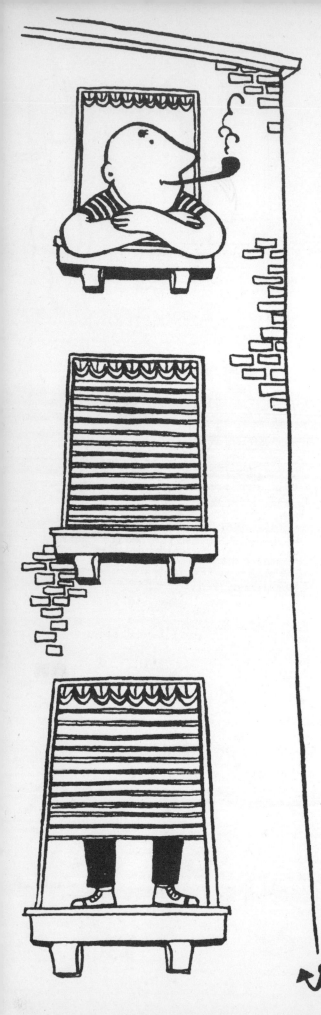

"Notice how they always show the best parts in the trailers."

STARKE, LILLIPUT, ENGLAND

AL KAUFMAN, MACLEAN'S, CANADA

FISCHER, NEUE ILLUSTRIERTE, GERMANY

GANTRIIS, LILLIPUT, ENGLAND

GALLAGHER, SAGA, U. S.

89

THELWELL, LONDON OPINION, ENGLAND

RONALD SEARLE, ENGLAND

"Stick'em up!"

JACK MAXWELL, PARIS-MATCH, FRANCE

FEYER, MACLEAN'S CANADA

90

MOROSETTI, IL TRAVASO, ITALY

"It's a boy!"

MOFREY, SAMEDI-SOIR, FRANCE

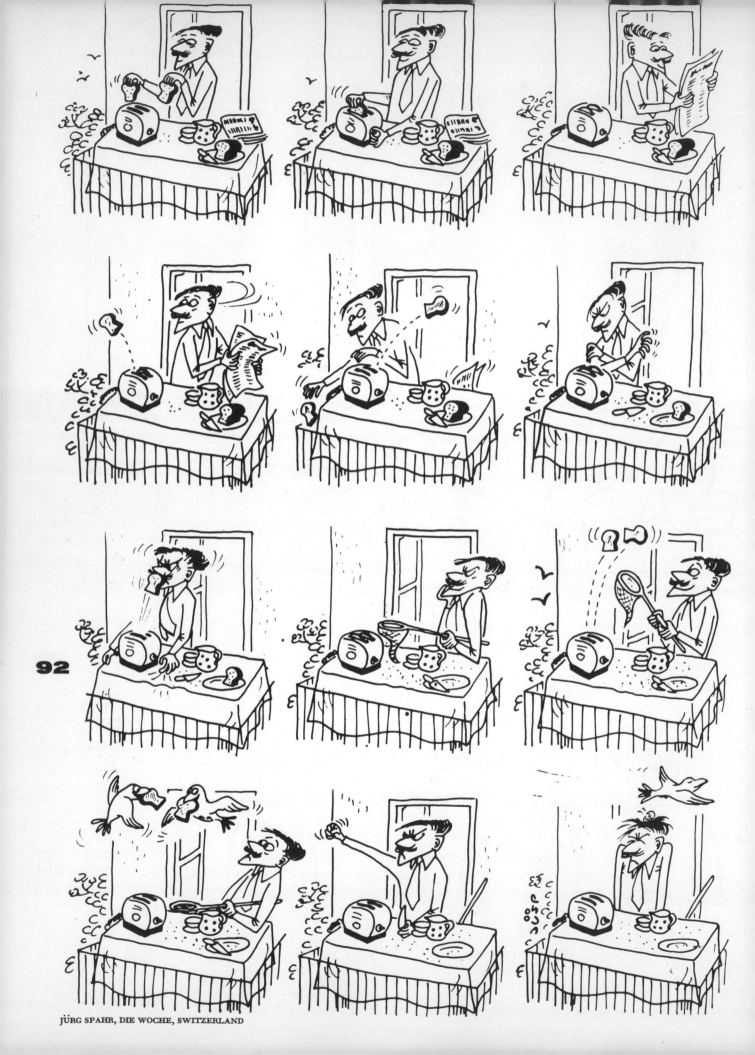

92

SPOHR, DER STERN, GERMANY

BERTHAU, DER STERN, GERMANY

93

"Alone at last! . . . It's wonderful to be able to chat a little without feeling that your mother is behind us."

JEAN BELLUS, FRANCE DIMANCHE, FRANCE

JÜRG SPAHR, NEBELSPALTER, SWITZERLAND

SMILBY, LILLIPUT, ENGLAND

"When are you going to fix the elevator?"

BORTOLATO, SETTIMO GIORNO, ITALY

"Well, you didn't make it, Slick—but it certainly was an interesting jail break."

GALLAGHER, THE SATURDAY EVENING POST, U. S.

95

JACK MAXWELL, IL TRAVASO, ITALY

FEYER, MACLEAN'S, CANADA

"They're having quite a time expelling Figley."

AL JOHNS, THIS WEEK, U. S.

JÜRG SPAHR, MONSIEUR, SWITZERLAND

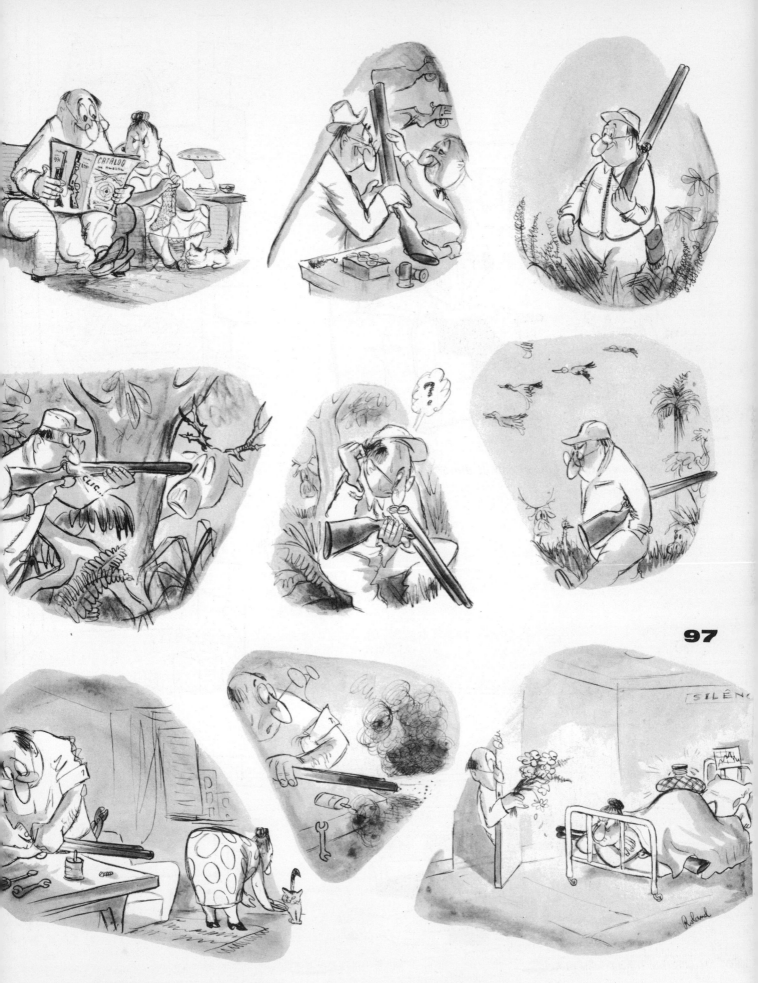

97

ROLAND, MANCHETE, BRAZIL

"What have you got there—a new pair of shoes?"

FRANK O'NEAL, COLLIER'S, U. S.

98

"How's that for a tricky punch?"

FRANK RIDGEWAY, THE SATURDAY EVENING POST, U. S.

1.

2.

3.

4.

SHIRVANIAN, THE SATURDAY EVENING POST, U. S.

"Do you think you're the only one who thinks about all the men you could have married?"

BLAKLEY, THE SATURDAY EVENING POST, U. S.

1.

2.

3

99

"See anything you like?"

LAMB, SAGA, U. S.

4

AAGAARD —

AAGAARD, THE SATURDAY EVENING POST, U. S.

100

SUNDAY MORNING

EMETT, LIFE, U.S.

SIM, LA PRESSE, FRANCE

101

"My mom would like to borrow 2 cups of flour, 2 teaspoons of baking powder, 2 eggs, cup an' a half sugar . . .!"

"My mom would like to borrow 4 pieces of cake!"

RENÉ CHAG, SAMEDI-SOIR, FRANCE

102

ANDRÉ FRANÇOIS, FRANCE

MÜLLER, HET PAROOL, THE NETHERLANDS

SIM, LE HÉRISSON, FRANCE

103

104

HIERARCHY

ANDRÉ FRANÇOIS, FRANCE

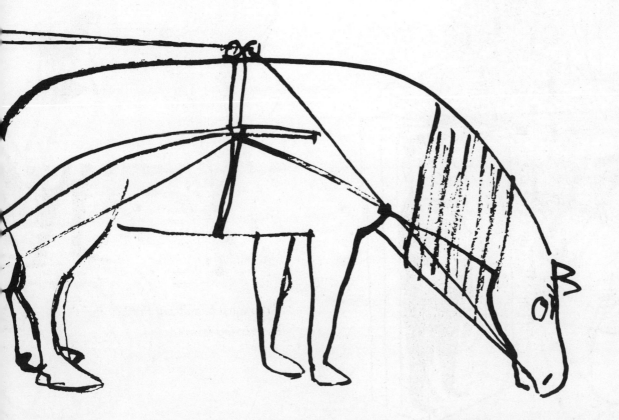

105

André François

106

TON SMITS

"*Step outside and say that!*"

MARKUS

MARKUS, DER STERN, GERMANY

BOSC

BOSC, PARIS-MATCH, FRANCE

G. PIANI

G. PIANI, NAZIONE SERA, ITALY

107

Hewison

HEWISON, LILLIPUT, ENGLAND

1.

2.

3.

4.

108

5.

BILL
HARRISON

MOFREY, SAMEDI-SOIR, FRANCE

110

RONALD SEARLE, ENGLAND

"About time for the news."

"On account of the big snow expected tonight, there will be no school tomorrow . . . I repeat . . . no school tomorrow."

BILL HARRISON, SUCCESSFUL FARMING, U. S.

"The condemned's a friend of the executioner."

CONSIGLI, IL TRAVASO, ITALY

111

"Now repeat after me: 'Fellow scientists, we are gathered here today...'"

GALLAGHER, COLLIER'S, U. S.

BORTOLATO, IL TRAVASO, ITALY

112

SIMPKINS, MACLEAN'S, CANADA

SIM, SAMEDI-SOIR, FRANCE

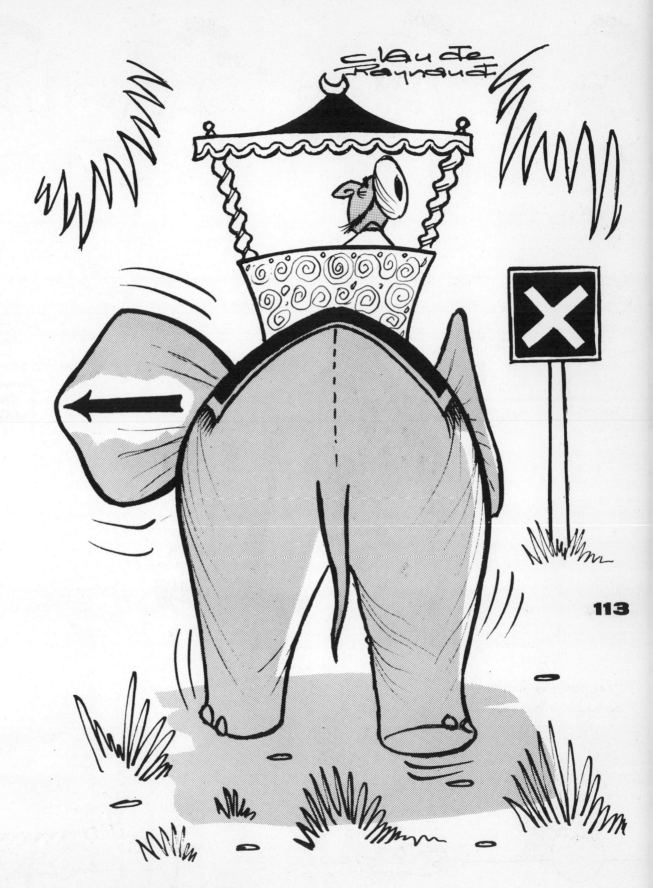

113

CLAUDE RAYNAUD, LA PRESSE, FRANCE

CONSIGLI, IL TRAVASO, ITALY

114

"The choice of ground is mine."

BORTOLATO, IL TRAVASO, ITALY

TON SMITS, MACLEAN'S, CANADA

JACK MAXWELL, PARIS-MATCH, FRANCE

115

FEYER, MACLEAN'S, CANADA

JÜRG SPAHR, SWITZERLAND

116

JACQUES FAIZANT, FRANCE DIMANCHE, FRANCE

"She doesn't want a man to take her."

SIVIC, REDBOOK, U. S.

"Ooooooh, say can you see—by the dawn's early light
—what so proudly we hail—at the twilight's last ..."

AL JOHNS, THE SATURDAY EVENING POST, U. S.

"Mother told me there would be knights like this."

LOCKE, NATION'S BUSINESS, U. S.

"But if I said it was good, you'd only cook the same
thing again."

M. BLANCHARD, LADIES' HOME JOURNAL, U. S.

MOROSETTI, L'EUROPEO, ITALY

"According to your weight you should be nine feet, six and one half inches tall."

HARRY MACE, THE SATURDAY EVENING POST, U. S.

GUY BARA, ICI PARIS, FRANCE

STARKE, LILLIPUT, ENGLAND

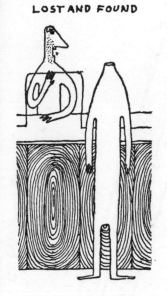

*"Yes, a head has just been
turned in."*

G. PIANI, NAZIONE SERA,
ITALY

THE END OF THE CONCERT

MOROSETTI, L'EUROPEO, ITALY

FEYER, MACLEAN'S, CANADA

120

"*We must be on Mercury!*"

CÉSAR, CANARD ENCHAÎNÉ, FRANCE

TON SMITS, MACLEAN'S, CANADA

MARKUS

MARKUS, GERMANY

LEON, DER STERN, GERMANY

HOLBEK, HUDIBRAS, DENMARK

121

FEYER, MACLEAN'S, CANADA

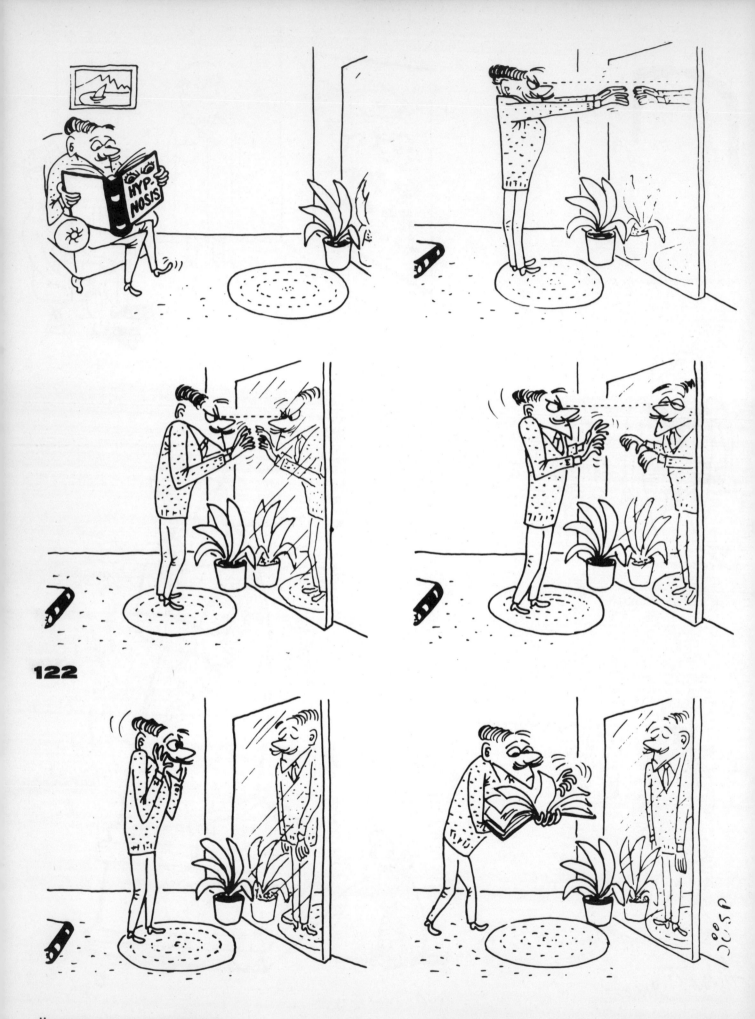

122

JÜRG SPAHR, DIE WOCHE, SWITZERLAND

123

André François

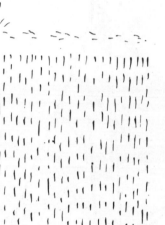

124

JÜRG SPAHR, NEBELSPALTER, SWITZERLAND

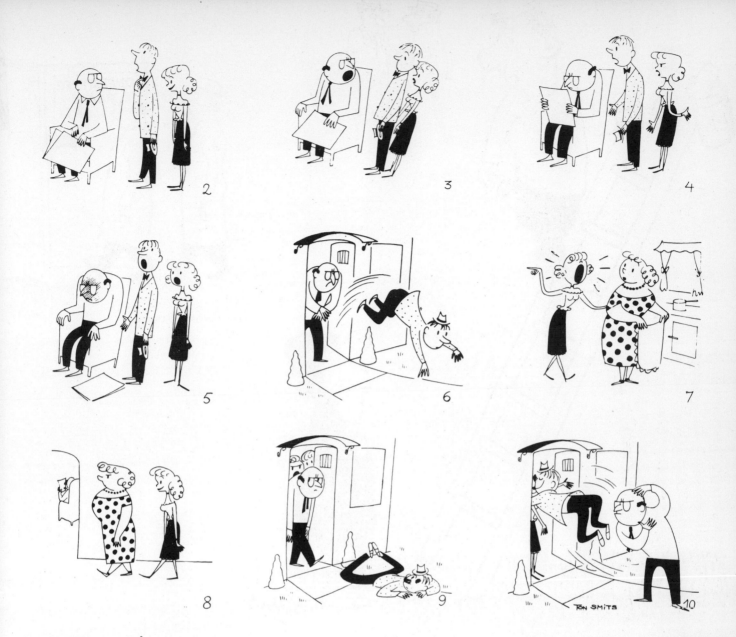

TON SMITS, COLLIER'S, U. S.

BORTOLATO, LE ORE, ITALY

EARL, ANSWERS, ENGLAND

"Of course *you can't see the house—I haven't* painted *it yet!*"

THAVES, SAGA, U. S.

JÜRG SPAHR, DIE WOCHE, SWITZERLAND

J. M. JACKSON, © PUNCH, ENGLAND

"One, two, three . . . I'm coming!"

WOLTER, NEUE ILLUSTRIERTE, GERMANY

"Next window, please."

G. PIANI, IL TRAVASO, ITALY

"Mrs. Briggs, can Bobby come out and play?"

AL KAUFMAN, MACLEAN'S, CANADA

JÜRG SPAHR, DIE WOCHE, SWITZERLAND

128

FEYER, MACLEAN'S, CANADA

"And this is Rachel—our head girl."

RONALD SEARLE, ENGLAND

129

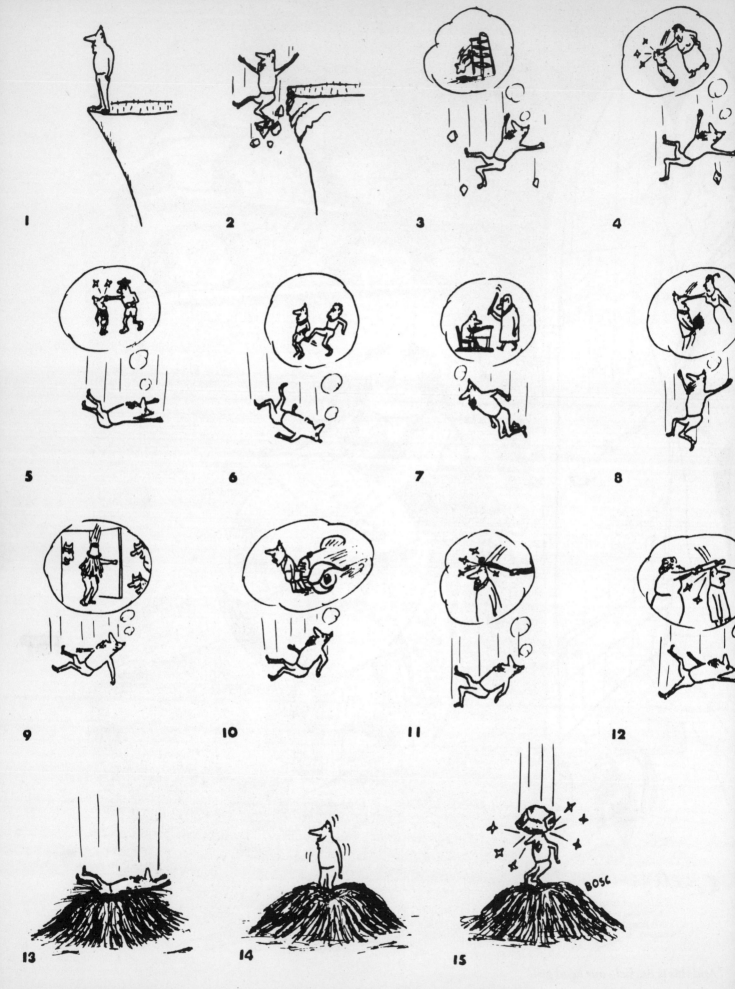

JOHN FRAZER, THE TEXAS RANGER, U. S.

"Almost human, aren't they?"

TED SCORFIELD, THE SYDNEY BULLETIN, AUSTRALIA

"Oh, for heaven's sake, Joe!"

MOROSETTI, L'EUROPEO, ITALY

132

ARNE, HUDIBRAS, DENMARK

JEAN DEJOUX, PARIS-MATCH, FRANCE

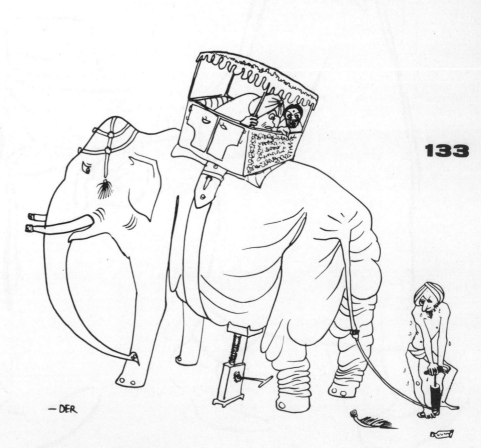

TETSU, LE RIRE, FRANCE

133

LOTHAR URSINUS
NEUE ILLUSTRIERTE, GERMANY

ERNEMANN SANDER, GERMANY

134

"*I'm doing a self-portrait.*"

MAURICE HENRY, FRANCE

BOSC, FRANCE DIMANCHE, FRANCE

136

THE SULTAN'S GOUT

MALAGOLA, ITALY

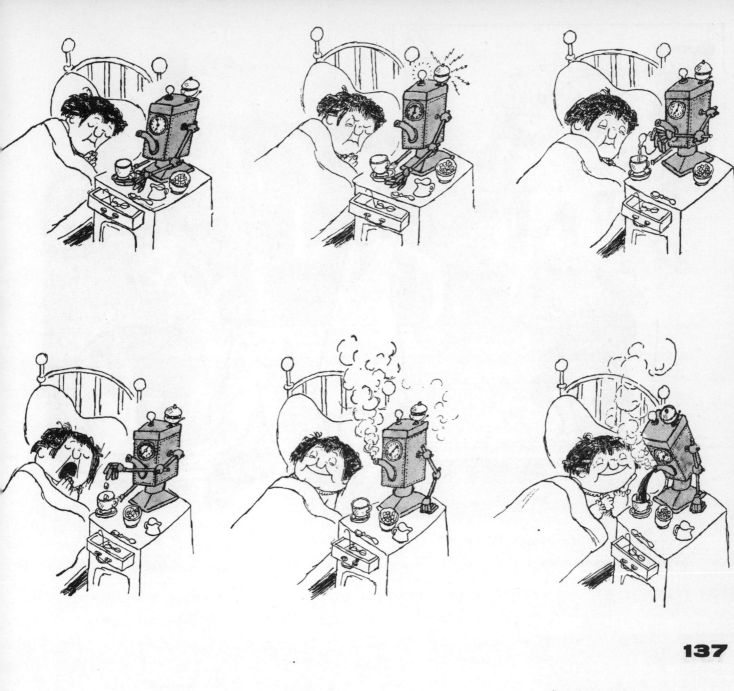

137

"I can passively resist any man in the house!"

138

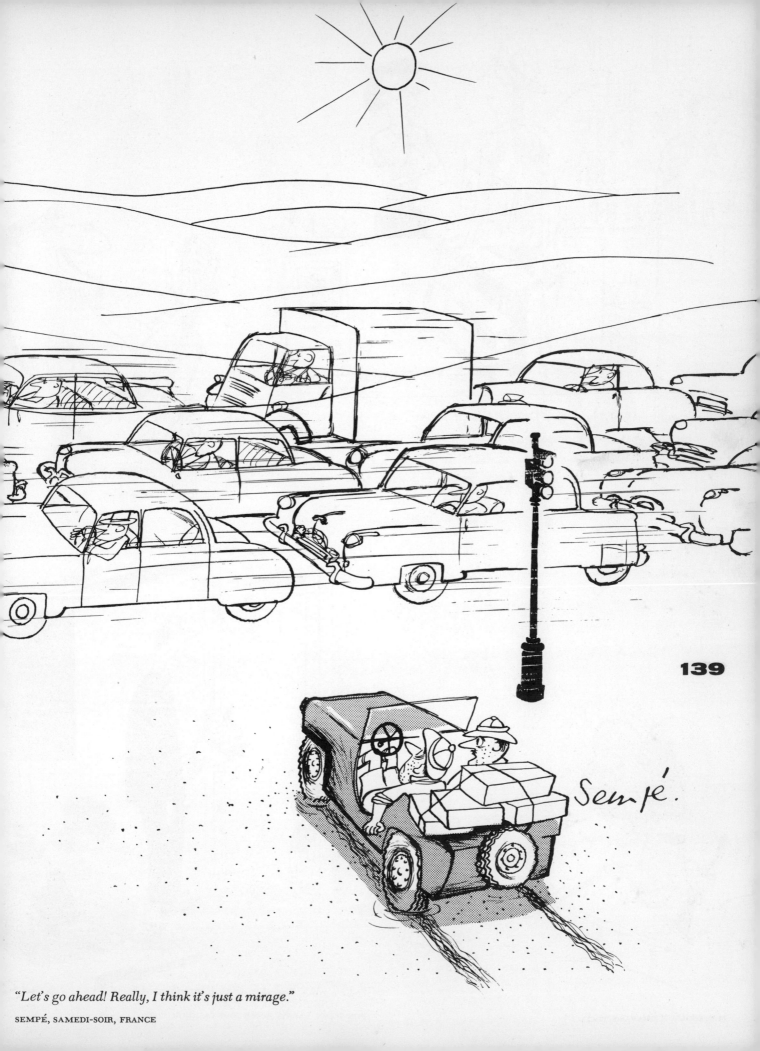

"*Let's go ahead! Really, I think it's just a mirage.*"

SEMPÉ, SAMEDI-SOIR, FRANCE

"I don't suppose you'd have any 'Do-It-HERself books?"

RODRIGUES, NEW YORK TIMES BOOK REVIEW, U. S.

JENNY DALENOORD, HET PAROOL,

THE NETHERLANDS

140

"She's gone. You shouldn't have phoned first."

FEYER, MACLEAN'S, CANADA

DON TOBIN, LADIES' HOME JOURNAL, U. S.

THE WRITING PUBLIC...

1. *Dear Sir,*
   "... your last letter was so encouraging may I be so bold as to ..."

2. *Lord Glengravy presents his compliments and hopes that you will favour enclosed with publication.*

141

HANS FISCHER, ZEIT UND BILD, GERMANY

3. "... if the enclosed MS. is not accepted will you please tell me why? To save your valuable time I have enclosed a chart containing fifteen alternative reasons for rejection. Will you please check those that apply?"

4. "... although I am onley fifteen..."

5. "This really happened ..."

"I can't help it. It's part of the hospital's economy drive."

PIT, I B Z ILLUSTRIERTE, GERMANY

6. "... I claim the distinction of being the possessor of a record collection of rejection slips. If an article on such a subject would be acceptable might I ...?"

7. "... I write for my own enjoyment, but my friends think these very funny and have persuaded me to send them to you ..."

8. "I am beginning to wonder if editors are human ..."

RONALD SEARLE, ENGLAND

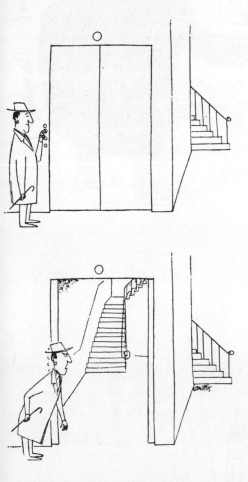

GANTRIIS, HUDIBRAS, DENMARK

143

"You're the first man to lay a hand on me."

GANTRIIS, HUDIBRAS, DENMARK

"How much is that one there?"

SEMPÉ, ICI PARIS, FRANCE

144

HANS FISCHER, DER STERN, GERMANY

AL JOHNS, THE SATURDAY EVENING POST, U. S.

LUNØE, HUDIBRAS, DENMARK

145

TON SMITS, THIS WEEK, U. S.

The Viola (pizzicato)

The Violin Double

The Bassethorn

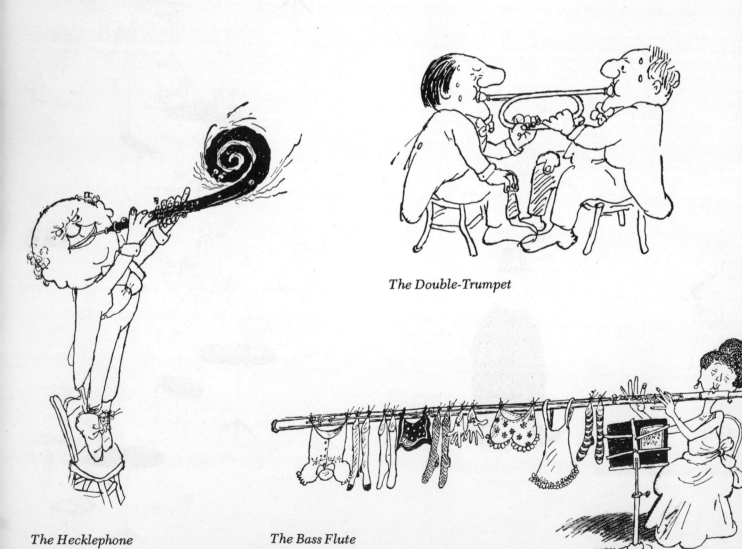

The Double-Trumpet

The Hecklephone

The Bass Flute

The Bass Trombone

The Contra-Bassoon

The Harp

147

The Kettle Drums

The Oboe

HOLBEK, HUDIBRAS, DENMARK

FRANZ FÜCHSEL, NA, NORWAY

"What are you screaming for? He won't eat you. Dinosaurs are herbivorous."

GUGLIELMO GUASTA, IL SETTEBELLO, ITALY

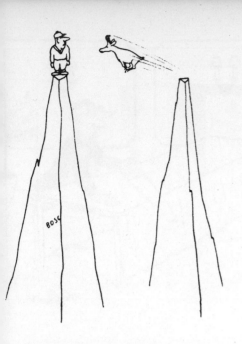

BOSC, PARIS-MATCH, FRANCE

149

JØRGEN MOGENSEN, PARIS-MATCH, FRANCE

TETSU, ICI PARIS, FRANCE

1

2

150

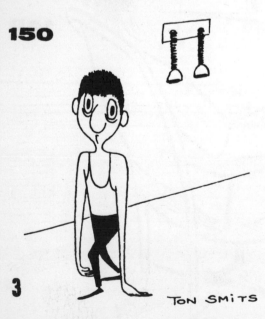

3

TON SMITS

TON SMITS, THIS WEEK, U. S.

"A table for two."

JØRGEN MOGENSEN, HUDIBRAS, DENMARK

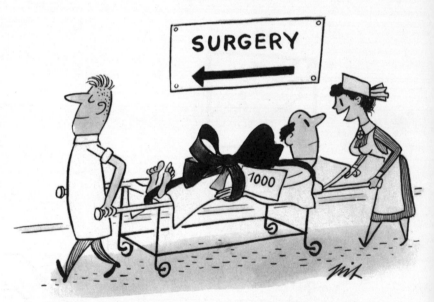

"You're the chief's one thousandth appendectomy."

PIT, I B Z ILLUSTRIERTE; GERMANY

THE HAUT MONDE: HUNTING AT HOME

PIT, IL TRAVASO, ITALY

HANS FISCHER, DER STERN, GERMANY

AL KAUFMAN, THE SATURDAY REVIEW, U. S.

152

Quiz: Which man has just returned from his vacation?

MALAGOLA, IL TRAVASO, ITALY

GANTRIIS, HUDIBRAS, DENMARK

TETSU, FRANCE DIMANCHE, FRANCE

154

FRANZ FÜCHSEL, SE, SWEDEN

"Bedtime? Already?"

TON SMITS, THIS WEEK, U. S.

JEAN DEJOUX, PARIS-MATCH, FRANCE

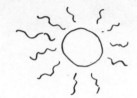

155

RONALD SEARLE, ENGLAND

JÜRG SPAHR, MONSIEUR, SWITZERLAND

TOM ROBERTS, CALIFORNIA PELICAN, U. S.

156

HERVÉ, FRANCE DIMANCHE, FRANCE

BOSC, FRANCE DIMANCHE, FRANCE

"Here's a good one. On the trumpet solo the man downstairs bangs on the ceiling."

LOCKE, NATION'S BUSINESS, U. S.

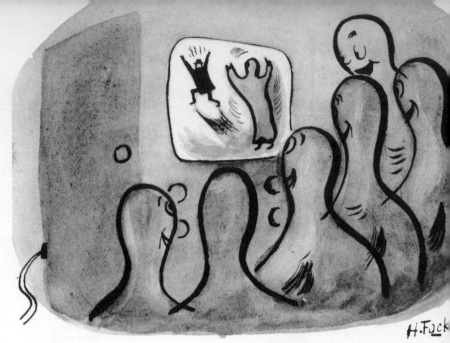

HERMAN FOCKE, REVUE, GERMANY

158

"Excuse me, madam, but your husband is three beds down."

PIT, I B Z ILLUSTRIERTE, GERMANY

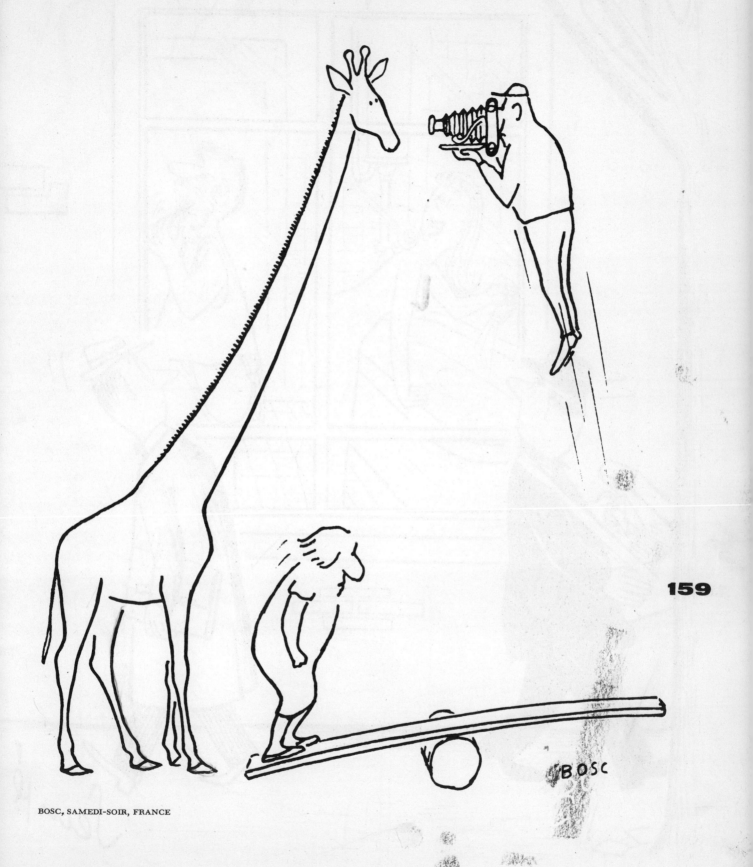

BOSC, SAMEDI-SOIR, FRANCE

159

"It's a very special kind of window glass. The man who sold it to me explained that it lets us see the people passing by on the street, but they can't see us."

SEMPÉ, SAMEDI-SOIR, FRANCE

MAURICE HENRY, FRANCE

VIRGIL PARTCH, COLLIER'S, U. S.

NORMANNO

"Which side do you want to sit on, dear?"
"It doesn't matter. I'm ambidextrous."

NORMANNO, IL TRAVASO, ITALY

162

SEMPÉ, SAMEDI-SOIR, FRANCE

HANS FISCHER, ZEIT UND BILD, GERMANY

LOGICAL CONCLUSIONS

"I began with butterflies, too!"

BORTOLATO, LE ORE, ITALY

164

H. J. BRANDES, NEUE ILLUSTRIERTE, GERMANY

LALIT S. BOOCH, THE TIMES OF INDIA, INDIA

165

"Buy me. I know lots of dirty stories!"

166

SUNDOWN

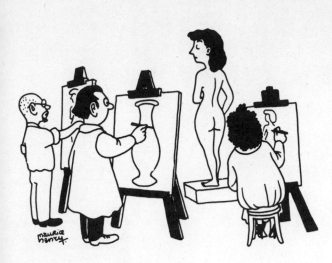

MAURICE HENRY, FRANCE

TON SMITS

TON SMITS, COLLIER'S, U.S.

"Please, Pastor, can't we keep him
until the new bell tower is ready?"

WOLTER, LUSTIGE ILLUSTRIERTE,
GERMANY

167

JULES STAUBER, WOCHENEND, GERMANY

168

"All right, where's the boy who was mucking about with hydrogen
in science class this morning?"

GILES, LONDON DAILY EXPRESS, ENGLAND

RONALD SEARLE, ENGLAND

TON SMITS, THIS WEEK, U. S.

170

TETSU, FRANCE DIMANCHE, FRANCE

"*Now here's a set that has proved very popular . . .*"

ENGLISH, MACLEAN'S, CANADA

PIT, I B Z ILLUSTRIERTE, GERMANY

171

"*I wouldn't stand over there, son.*"

DANA FRADON, ARGOSY, U. S.

COSPER, HUDIBRAS, DENMARK

172

AMBUSH

BORTOLATO, VISTO, ITALY

"Your allergy tests suggest that you may have been intended for some other planet."

WALT WETTERBERG, THE SATURDAY EVENING POST, U. S.

"I must be immortal."

HEIDEMANN, QUICK, GERMANY

TETSU, LE RIRE, FRANCE

AL KAUFMAN, THE SATURDAY EVENING POST, U. S.

GRAGE-

"*I have an unlisted number.*"

GRAGE, SE, SWEDEN

175

FEYER, MACLEAN'S, CANADA

ENGLISH, MACLEAN'S, CANADA

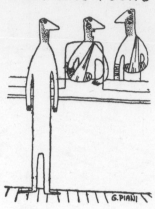

"Here is the mastiff's owner."

G. PIANI, NAZIONE SERA, ITALY

PIT, I B Z ILLUSTRIERTE, GERMANY

JEAN MARC, SAMEDI-SOIR, FRANCE

177

"Second floor, please."

HANS FISCHER, ZEIT UND BILD, GERMANY

MOROSETTI, IL TRAVASO, ITALY

"That's a nice thing to call a baby on the first day of National Baby Week."

GILES, LONDON DAILY EXPRESS, ENGLAND

178

GANTRIIS, HUDIBRAS, DENMARK

JØRGEN MOGENSEN, PARIS-MATCH, FRANCE

THE SEASON OF LOVE

"No use, they've been married too long."

"As soon as I saw you, love touched my heart."

"Nobody could be that bashful!"

GUY BARA, ICI PARIS, FRANCE

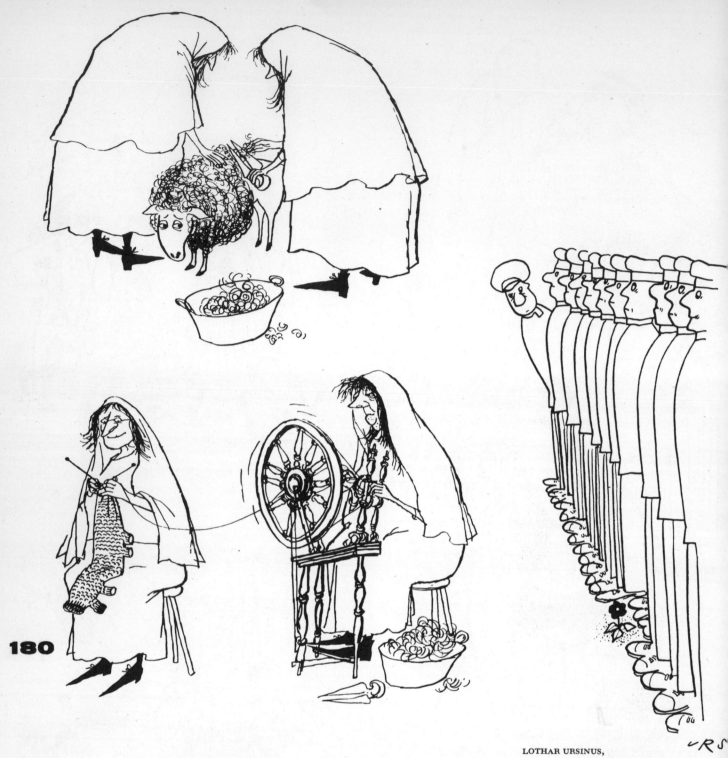

180

LOTHAR URSINUS,
NEUE ILLUSTRIERTE, GERMANY

RONALD SEARLE, ENGLAND

"Haircut, shave, wave."
ROLAND STIGULINSKY, DEUTSCHE ILLUSTRIERTE, GERMANY

"EXPLOSION"

CANZLER, NEUE ILLUSTRIERTE, GERMANY

181

TETSU, NOIR ET BLANC, FRANCE

"This apartment house looks as though it had never been repaired."
"That's right. It's just been built."

E. SHCHEGLOV, KROKODIL, U. S. S. R.

182

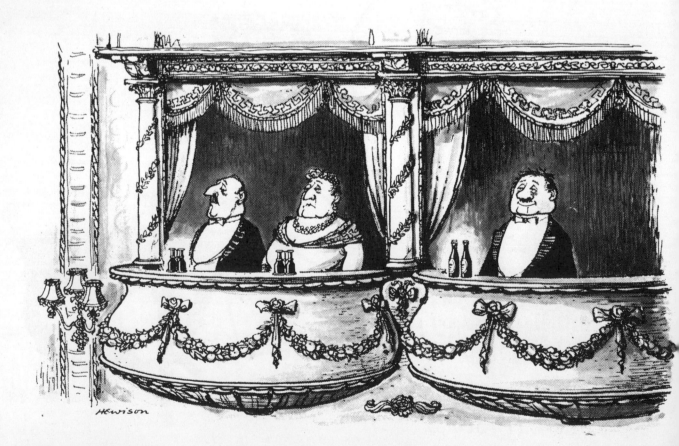

183

JÜRG SPAHR, DIE WOCHE, SWITZERLAND

ROLAND, MANCHETE, BRAZIL

"Onward, into darkest Africa!"

GANTRIIS, HUDIBRAS, DENMARK

GUY VALLS, ICI PARIS, FRANCE

185

"No, Johnny can't come out and play. He's being punished!"

BERTHAU, DER STERN, GERMANY

"Fish, fish, nothing but fish! If I could only catch my other shoe."

LIMMROTH, FRANKFURTER ILLUSTRIERTE, GERMANY

HERMAN FOCKE, MANDRIL, THE NETHERLANDS

186

COSPER, HUDIBRAS, DENMARK

PHOTOGRAPHIC SOUVENIR OF THE ESCAPE

MAURICE HENRY, FRANCE

"*That's my geometry teacher.*"

FACKE, FRANKFURTER ILLUSTRIERTE, GERMANY

ELZI, SIE UND ER, SWITZERLAND

188

LIMMROTH, KRISTALL ILLUSTRIERTE, GERMANY

BALTHASAR LIPPISCH, MÜNCHNER ILLUSTRIERTE, GERMANY

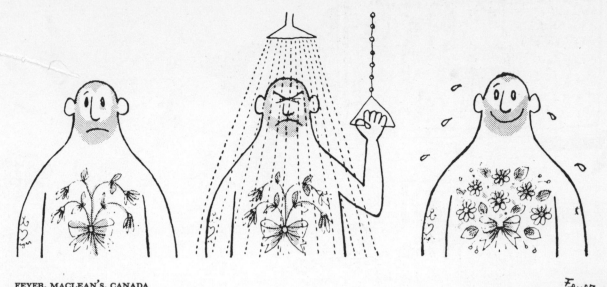

FEYER, MACLEAN'S, CANADA

Feyer

SEMPÉ, SAMEDI-SOIR, FRANCE

189

HERMAN FOCKE,
MANDRIL, THE NETHERLANDS

190

JÜRG SPAHR, MONSIEUR, SWITZERLAND

ELZI, SIE UND ER, SWITZERLAND

CONSIGLI, IL TRAVASO, ITALY

191

"How's the water?"

TETSU, FRANCE DIMANCHE, FRANCE

THE UNMASKING

STREIT, DER STERN, GERMANY

"I wish I could travel to foreign lands and see all of those tractors and other modern farm machinery we invented."

FRANZ FÜCHSEL, SE, SWEDEN

192

THE DUEL

BORTOLATO, IL TRAVASO, ITALY

"All right, hand it over."

DOMINIQUE SAND, FRANCE DIMANCHE, FRANCE

"Sorry to be late, darling. I had insomnia."

MAURICE HENRY, FRANCE

193

MOALIC, SAMEDI-SOIR, FRANCE

UILIE, HET PAROOL, THE NETHERLANDS

194

"... You add mushrooms, pour in a glass of calvados, and then put in the cream..."

JEAN BELLUS, FRANCE DIMANCHE, FRANCE

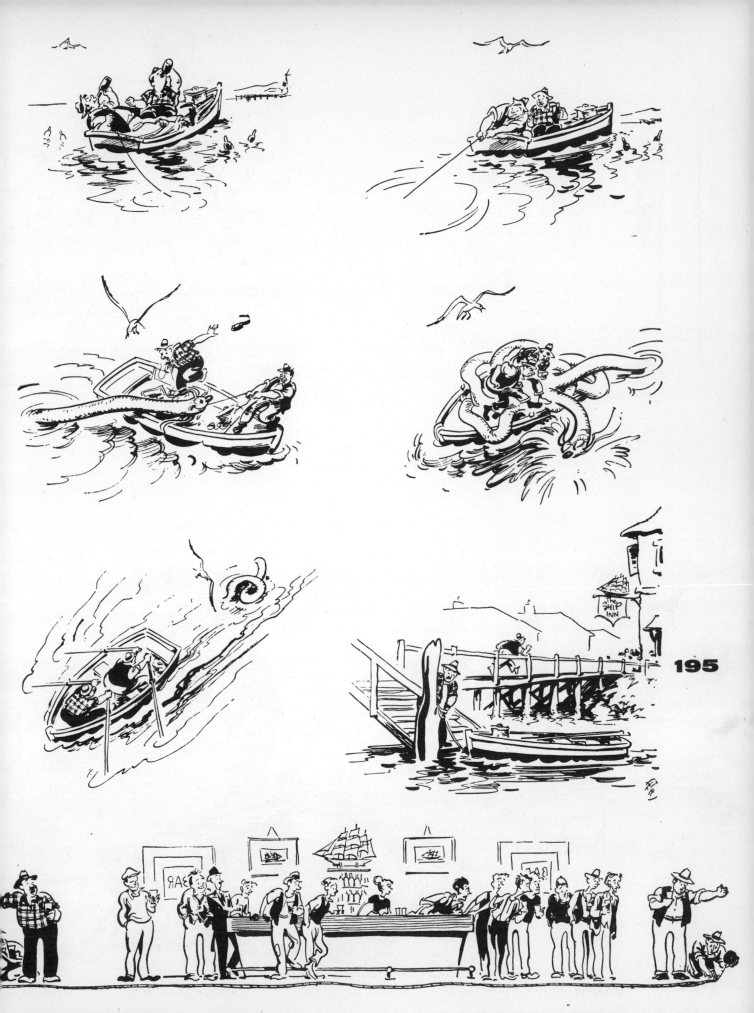

195

NORMAN HETHERINGTON, THE SYDNEY BULLETIN, AUSTRALIA

TREZ, PARIS-MATCH, FRANCE

HANS ULRICH MEURY, DIE WOCHE, SWITZERLAND

"That'll do! We don't want him to overshoot again!"

ERIC JOLLIFFE, PIX, AUSTRALIA

"They're chocolate..."

SEMPÉ, SAMEDI-SOIR, FRANCE

"What's for supper tonight?"

VIGHI, VIE NUOVE, ITALY

197

"I know how to say 'You drive me mad' in Italian."

CHON DAY, THIS WEEK, U. S.

SEMPÉ, SAMEDI-SOIR, FRANCE

198

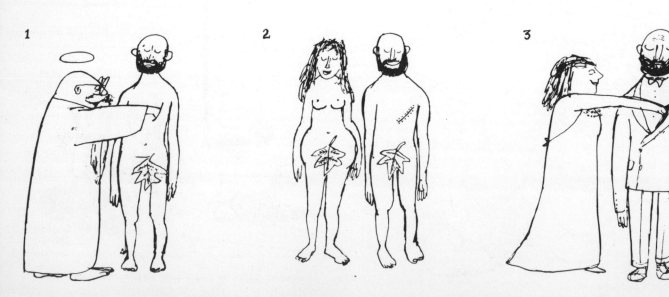

1

2

3

ANDRÉ FRANÇOIS, FRANCE

"It's for me."

EDGAR NORFIELD, MEN ONLY AND LONDON OPINION, ENGLAND

"Take it easy. When we're out of the city, then you can drive."

WIGG SIEGL, NEUE ILLUSTRIERTE, GERMANY

FECHNER, GERMANY

"*Ever have one of those days when everything seems to go wrong?*"

SIVIC, THE SATURDAY EVENING POST, U. S.

CUSTOMS

LIVE BEES

NASLUND, LEKTYR, SWEDEN

200

HANS ULRICH MEURY, DIE WOCHE, SWITZERLAND

"*A gentleman would like to talk to you on the telephone.*"

JEAN BELLUS, ICI PARIS, FRANCE

201

FECHNER, GERMANY

ELZI, SWITZERLAND

202

LOTHAR URSINUS, GERMANY

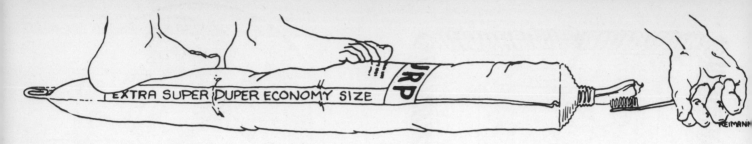

WILLIAM REIMANN, THE YALE RECORD, U. S.

204   ERIC BURGIN, © PUNCH, ENGLAND

A. F. WILES, © PUNCH, ENGLAND

CHAVAL, PARIS-MATCH, FRANCE

HEWISON, © PUNCH, ENGLAND

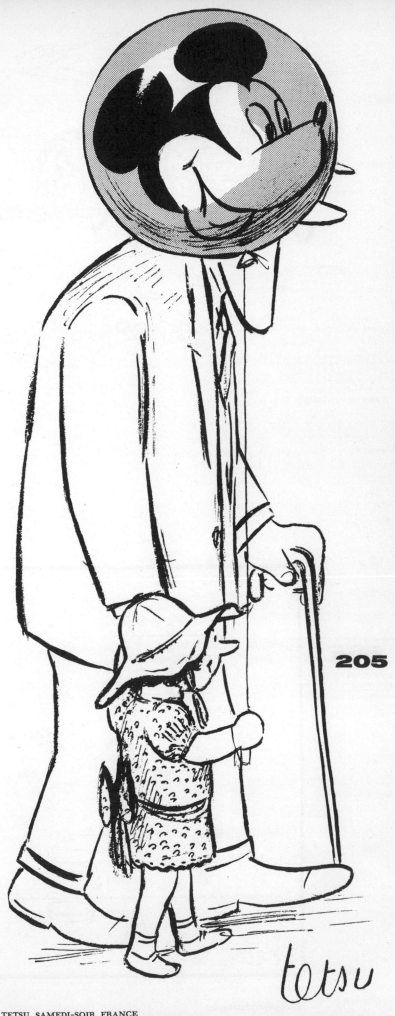

205

TETSU, SAMEDI-SOIR, FRANCE

ALAIN, COLLIER'S, U. S.

206

ELZI, SWITZERLAND

MINGOTE, A B C, SPAIN

207

"Their stupid games will make me catch my death of cold!"

GUY VALLS, ICI PARIS, FRANCE

BOSC, PARIS-MATCH, FRANCE

208

"There's a word you don't hear much any more."

HERB GREEN, THE SATURDAY EVENING POST, U. S.

ADAMSON, © PUNCH, ENGLAND

"Kerresswul!"

"Kaanzidin!"

"Shayyen!"

"Roslyn Gardens!"

BIL KEANE, THE SATURDAY EVENING POST, U. S.

F. KASTL, FRANKFURTER ILLUSTRIERTE, GERMANY

A. F. WILES, PUNCH, ENGLAND

210

MOSE, PARIS-MATCH, FRANCE

"You likely to be long with that 'orse?"

ERIC JOLLIFFE, PIX, AUSTRALIA

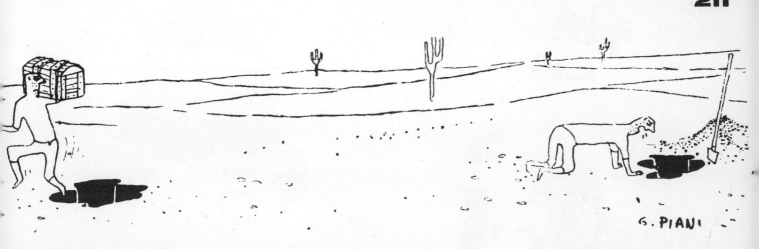

"Answer me! Is it the treasure or isn't it?"

G. PIANI, IL TRAVASO, ITALY

212

Just MARRIED

Photographer

Photographer

JØRGEN MOGENSEN, HUDIBRAS, DENMARK

tetsu

213

"*What little fish is going to be warm and cosy this winter?*"

TETSU, ICI PARIS, FRANCE

214

STAGE DOOR

HERMAN FOCKE, HET PAROOL, THE NETHERLANDS

DO NOT FEED THE BEARS

I AM NOT A BEAR

215

ROBERT DAY, SPORTS ILLUSTRATED, U.S.

THREE MEN AND A POLE

216

217

JACK MAXWELL, IL TRAVASO, ITALY

218

TETSU, SAMEDI-SOIR, FRANCE

CATRINUS, HET PAROOL, THE NETHERLANDS

"Ed's secretary has everything—no looks, no figure, no personality."

ROBERT HOYT, DUN'S REVIEW & MODERN INDUSTRY, U. S.

219

"And the clerk swore that this carpet wouldn't shrink!"

HEINZ BREN, WIENER ILLUSTRIERTE, AUSTRIA

"*I took a thorn out of his paw a few years back.*"

VIRGIL PARTCH, TRUE, U. S.

"*What's he supposed to be?*"

DAVE HIRSCH, AMERICAN MAGAZINE, U. S.

220

"*I started to make a ship, but I got bored.*"

BUNDFUSS, DEUTSCHE ILLUSTRIERTE, GERMANY

KLAUS PIELERT, NEUE ILLUSTRIERTE, GERMANY

"Winter's coming so I'm knitting him some long underwear."

RUDI FACKE, MÜNCHNER ILLUSTRIERTE, GERMANY

VIGHI, IL TRAVASO, ITALY

TETSU, FRANCE DIMANCHE, FRANCE

221

222

"This time it'd better be water!"

ERIC JOLLIFFE, PIX, AUSTRALIA

TREZ, SAMEDI-SOIR, FRANCE

TREZ, SAMEDI-SOIR, FRANCE

tetsu

TETSU, SAMEDI-SOIR, FRANCE

GRAHAM, © PUNCH, ENGLAND

CHAVAL, PARIS-MATCH, FRANCE

225

JERRY MARCUS, TRUE, U. S.

FECHNER, GERMANY

226

BOSC, PARIS-MATCH, FRANCE

BOB PETHICK, TRUE, U. S.

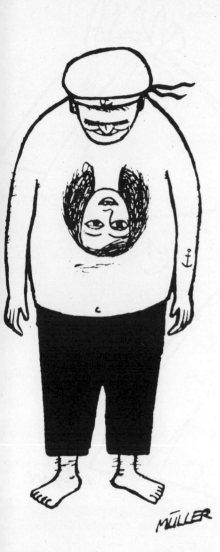

MÜLLER, HET PAROOL, THE NETHERLANDS

227

SEMPÉ, SAMEDI-SOIR, FRANCE

FLYING WALL CARPET

ELZI, DIE WOCHE, SWITZERLAND

228

RAYMOND PEYNET, FRANCE

"Get your hands up, Carson, or I'll blow your brains out!"

BOOTH, SAGA, U. S.

229

CAVALLO, L'EUROPEO, ITALY   LOTHAR URSINUS, GERMANY

"And a Merry Christmas to you."

STARKE, MEN ONLY, ENGLAND

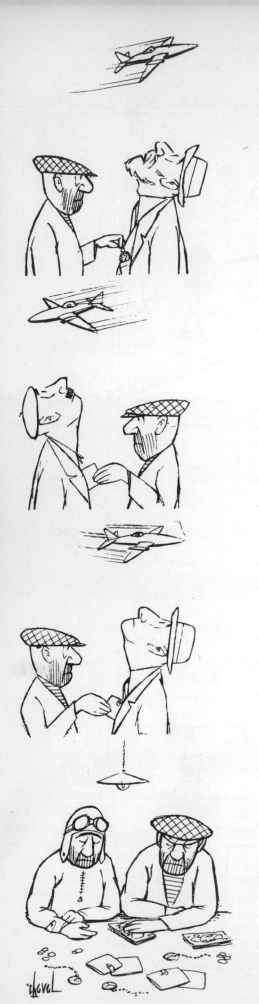

"Dammit. Here goes my Sundays."

CHAVAL, PARIS-MATCH, FRANCE   PAPLOW, SAGA, U. S.

231

PAPLOW, NEW YORK TIMES BOOK REVIEW, U. S.

232

SEMPÉ, FRANCE DIMANCHE, FRANCE

THE CHASE

VIGHI, VIE NUOVE, ITALY

MAURICE HENRY, FRANCE

233

RYUICHI YOKOYAMA, JAPAN

MALAGOLA, IL TRAVASO, ITALY

VACORI, IL TRAVASO, ITALY

"Yours?"

BILL DAVIS, STANFORD CHAPARRAL, U. S.

234

LEON, SE, SWEDEN

BOSC, PARIS-MATCH, FRANCE

"Dammit, I hit the starter button again!"

HEINZ BREN, WIENER ILLUSTRIERTE, AUSTRIA

235

RENÉ CHAG, SAMEDI-SOIR, FRANCE

"Do we need any milk today, Madeleine?"

CHAVAL, PARIS-MATCH, FRANCE

"Do you realize it has taken you twenty-five years to get dressed?"

SINÉ, PARIS-MATCH, FRANCE

236

SEMPÉ, SAMEDI-SOIR, FRANCE

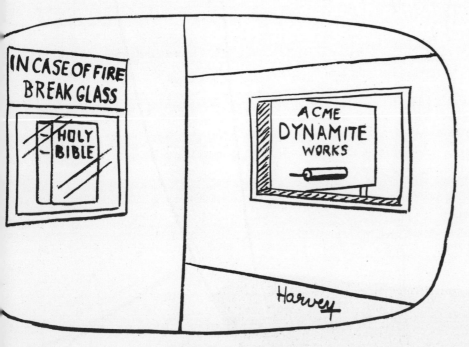

HARVEY, THE PRINCETON TIGER, U. S.

237

"That's the third ace he's served this set."

HARRIGAN, BRISBANE SUNDAY MAIL, AUSTRALIA

238

"I said: 'Full speed ahead!'"

HERVÉ, FRANCE DIMANCHE, FRANCE

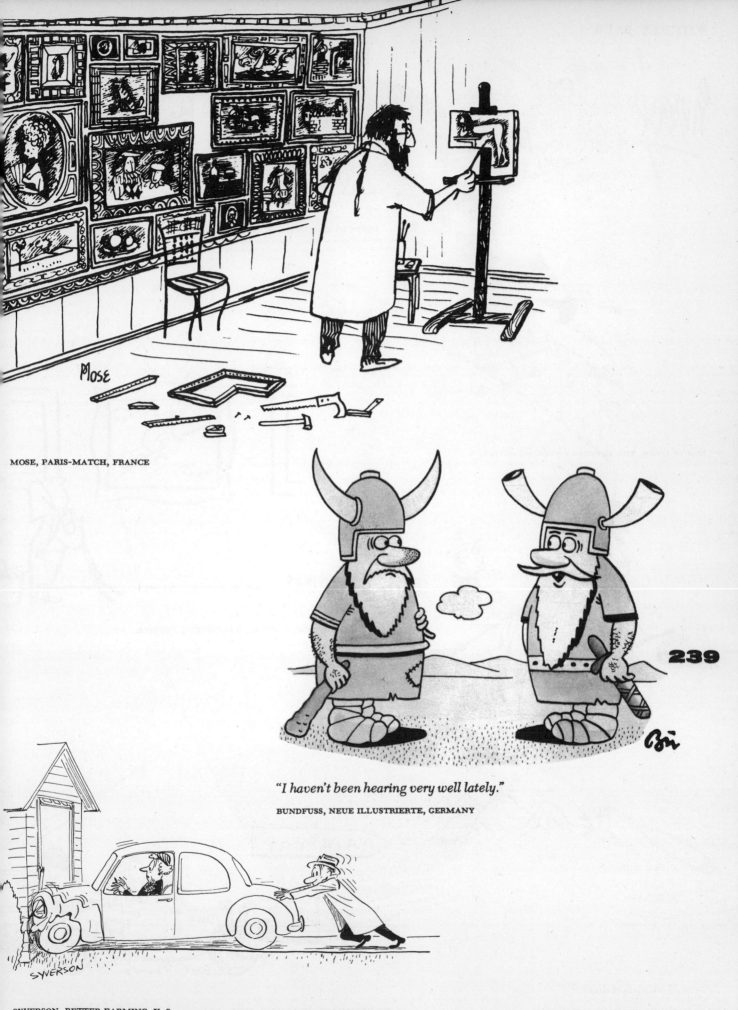

MOSE, PARIS-MATCH, FRANCE

239

"I haven't been hearing very well lately."

BUNDFUSS, NEUE ILLUSTRIERTE, GERMANY

SYVERSON, BETTER FARMING, U. S.

WITCHES' BREW

ERNST HEIDEMANN, DER STERN, GERMANY

MARTY LOWE

MARTY LOWE, THE SATURDAY EVENING POST, U. S.

KOS

KOS, WIENER ILLUSTRIERTE, AUSTRIA

240

DIETER KRESSEL, DER STERN, GERMANY

ERNST HEIDEMANN, DER STERN, GERMANY

"Yes, it's the very latest model."

ARIBERT NESSLINGER, DER STERN, GERMANY

"No, we didn't advertise for a cleaning woman."

FEYER, MACLEAN'S, CANADA

TON SMITS

TON SMITS, THIS WEEK, U. S.

WOLTER, LUSTIGE ILLUSTRIERTE, GERMANY

242

"I'm a little hard of hearing. What was it you dropped?"

HERVÉ, FRANCE

243

CANZLER, GERMANY

"It's the old story—joined to forget!"

ROWEL FRIERS, DUBLIN OPINION, IRELAND

FECHNER, GERMANY

ED HANSON, UNIVERSITY OF WASHINGTON COLUMNS, U.S.

"I'll take them."

JOHN ZIMA, CAVALIER, U. S.

"*This model is for older children; when you put her to bed, she closes her eyes and says 'Cheri.'*"

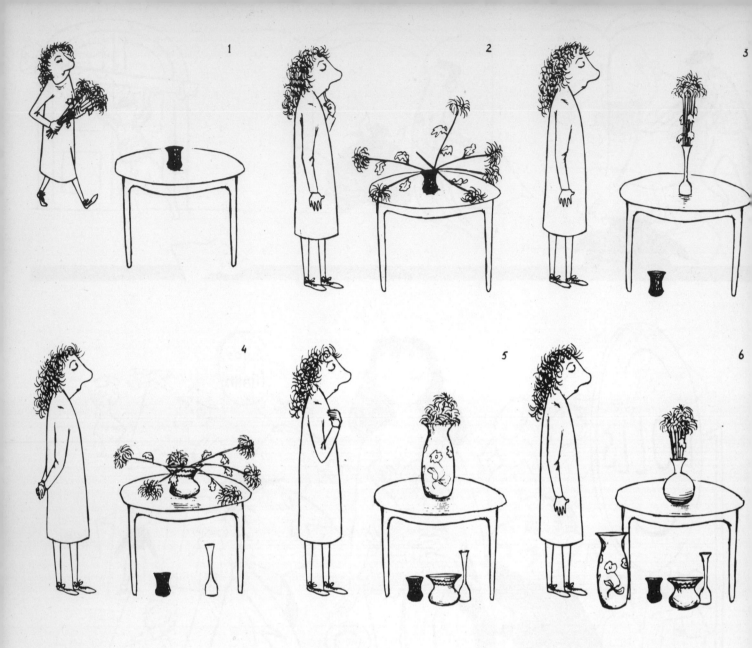

246

CATRINUS, HET PAROOL, THE NETHERLANDS

HELMUT HELLMESSEN,
NEUE ILLUSTRIERTE, GERMANY

CHAVAL, PARIS-MATCH, FRANCE

"*If Daddy has to go to jail, may I sleep in his bed tonight?*"

LARRY HARRIS, AMERICAN MAGAZINE, U. S.

JOHN SPAREY, CALIFORNIA PELICAN, U. S.

PAUL, SAMEDI-SOIR, FRANCE

248

"Be a good boy. Mother will be back soon."

B. LIPPISCH, BAVARIA VERLAG, GERMANY

VIGHI, VIE NUOVE, ITALY

IRONIMUS, MÜNCHNER ILLUSTRIERTE, GERMANY

249

"Oh, will I catch it when he comes down?"

SEMPÉ, SAMEDI-SOIR, FRANCE

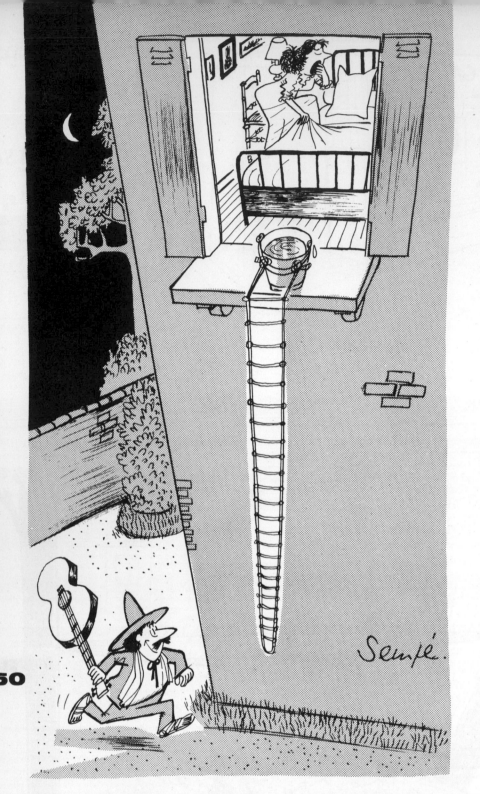

250

SEMPÉ, SAMEDI-SOIR, FRANCE

ERNST HEIDEMANN, GERMANY

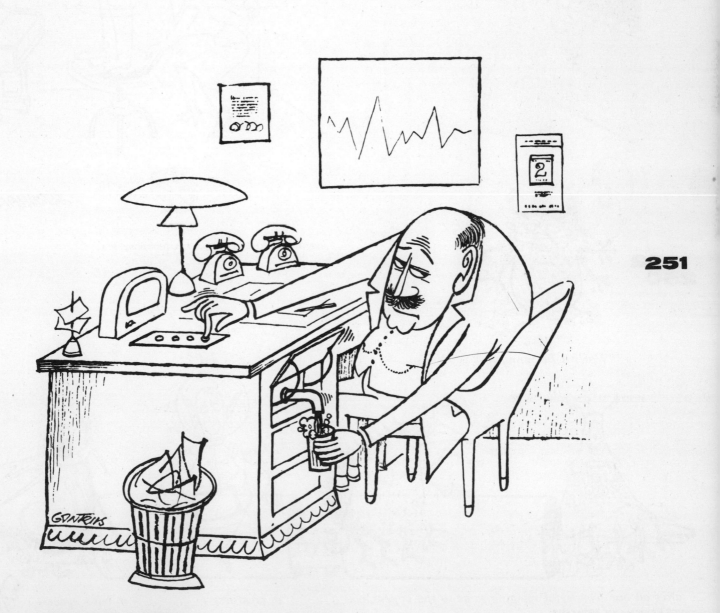

251

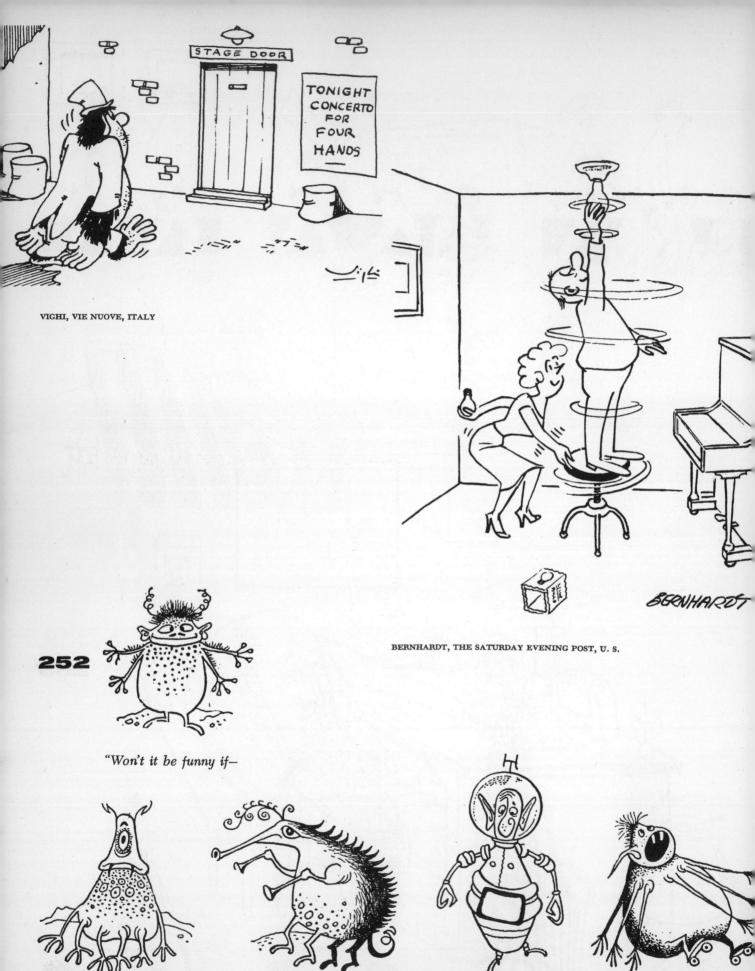

STAGE DOOR

TONIGHT
CONCERTO
FOR
FOUR
HANDS

VIGHI, VIE NUOVE, ITALY

BERNHARDT

252

BERNHARDT, THE SATURDAY EVENING POST, U. S.

"Won't it be funny if—

after all our wonderful imaginings as to the appearance—   of creatures—   in outer space—

BORTOLATO, L'EUROPEO, ITALY

253

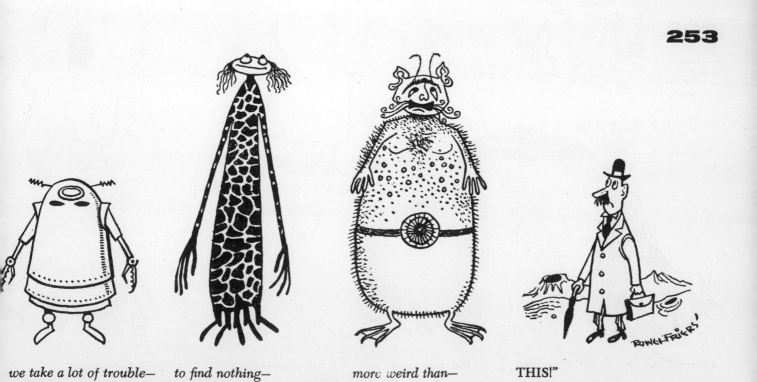

we take a lot of trouble— *to find nothing—* *more weird than—* **THIS!"**

ROWEL FRIERS, DUBLIN OPINION, IRELAND

254

"You needn't smell it, Mr. Barker—it's quite fresh."

"Life insurance department, please?

MOSE, PARIS-MATCH, FRANCE

256

"*You're certainly restless tonight.*"

HERVÉ, FRANCE DIMANCHE, FRANCE

"It's an automatic patent attorney!"

BOB BARNES, BALLYHOO, U. S.

257

"My advice to you, Hawkins, is to take the pins out of the map and stick them into the salesmen."

CHON DAY, THE SATURDAY EVENING POST, U. S.

"Looks pretty good, doesn't it, George?"

BOB BARNES, THE SATURDAY EVENING POST, U. S.

MAURICE HENRY, FRANCE

"WHERE IS EVERYONE?"

FRANK O'NEAL, COLLIER'S, U. S.

MINGOTE, A B C, SPAIN

RYUICHI YOKOYAMA, JAPAN

SIM, FRANCE DIMANCHE, FRANCE

259

"Do keep your hat on, sir."

MICHEL DOUAY, CARREFOUR, FRANCE

"The little darlings! They always share their presents."

GUY VALLS, ICI PARIS, FRANCE

MARKUS, MÜNCHNER ILLUSTRIERTE, GERMANY

261

LEON, DER STERN, GERMANY

4

5

CATRINUS, DE GROENE AMSTERDAMMER THE NETHERLANDS

1

2

262

3

4

"They couldn't afford a new car."

DUBOUT, ICI PARIS, FRANCE

NANDO, SETTIMO GIORNO, ITALY

"Take off your hat, son, when you pass a cemetery."

MOROSETTI, IL TRAVASO, ITALY

264

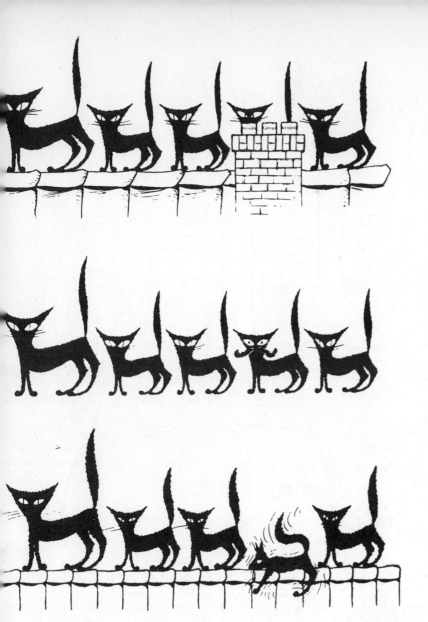

CATRINUS, DE GROENE AMSTERDAMMER, THE NETHERLANDS

JOHN COLE, TRUE, U. S.

265

HANS ULRICH MEURY, DIE WOCHE, SWITZERLAND

266

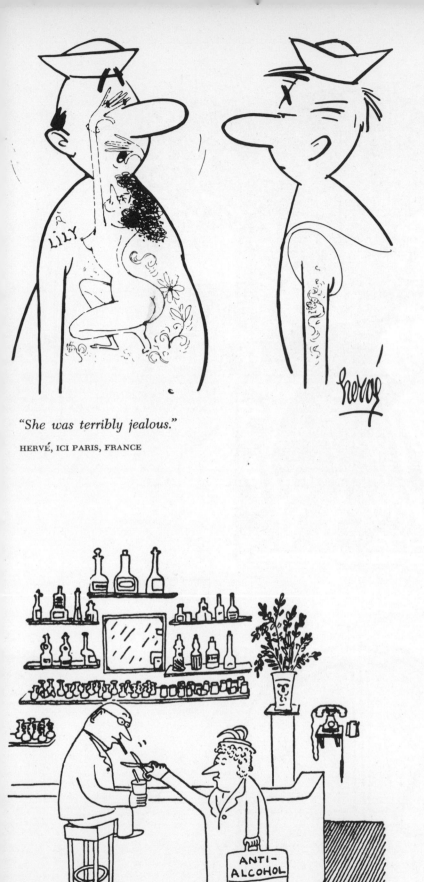

"She was terribly jealous."

HERVÉ, ICI PARIS, FRANCE

LAPLACE, ICI PARIS, FRANCE

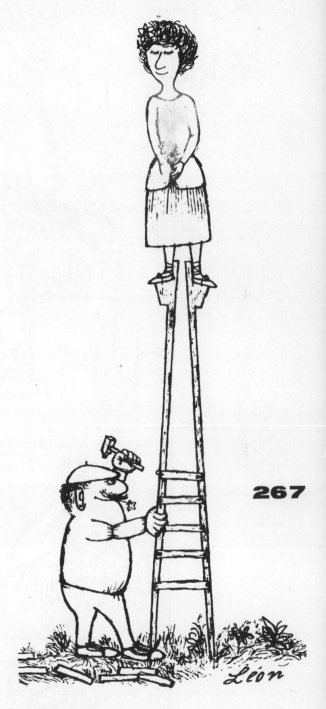

267

LEON, SE, SWEDEN

268

"... *Madam la Baronne du Machin de la Chose, His Excellency le Compte de Laglande* ..."

SIM, LE HÉRISSON, FRANCE

BORJALO, MANCHETE, BRAZIL

25¢
YOUR
PHOTO
WHILE
YOU
WAIT

STEIG, COLLIER'S, U. S.

269

BORJALO, MANCHETE, BRAZIL

270

MANFRED KREINER, WIENER BILDERWOCHE, AUSTRIA

ERIC BURGIN, © PUNCH, ENGLAND

HOFFNUNG, NEUE ILLUSTRIERTE, GERMANY

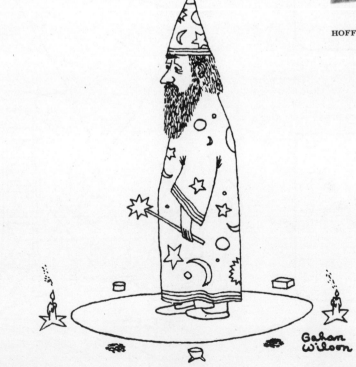

"If you use inferior materials you
get inferior demons ..."

GAHAN WILSON, COLLIER'S, U.S.

272

RYUICHI YOKOYAMA, JAPAN

"Play hairbrushes?"

SIGGS, © PUNCH, ENGLAND

PETER ESTIN, COLLIER'S, U. S.

RAYMOND PEYNET, FRANCE

273

BORJALO, MANCHETE, BRAZIL

MOROSETTI, SETTIMO GIORNO, ITALY

274

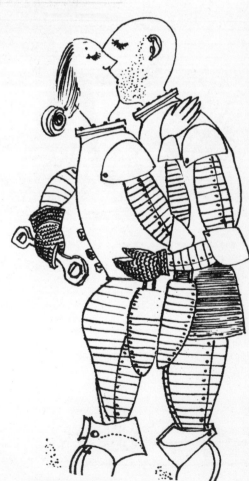

NANDO, SETTIMO GIORNO, ITALY

ERNST HEIDEMANN, DER STERN, GERMANY

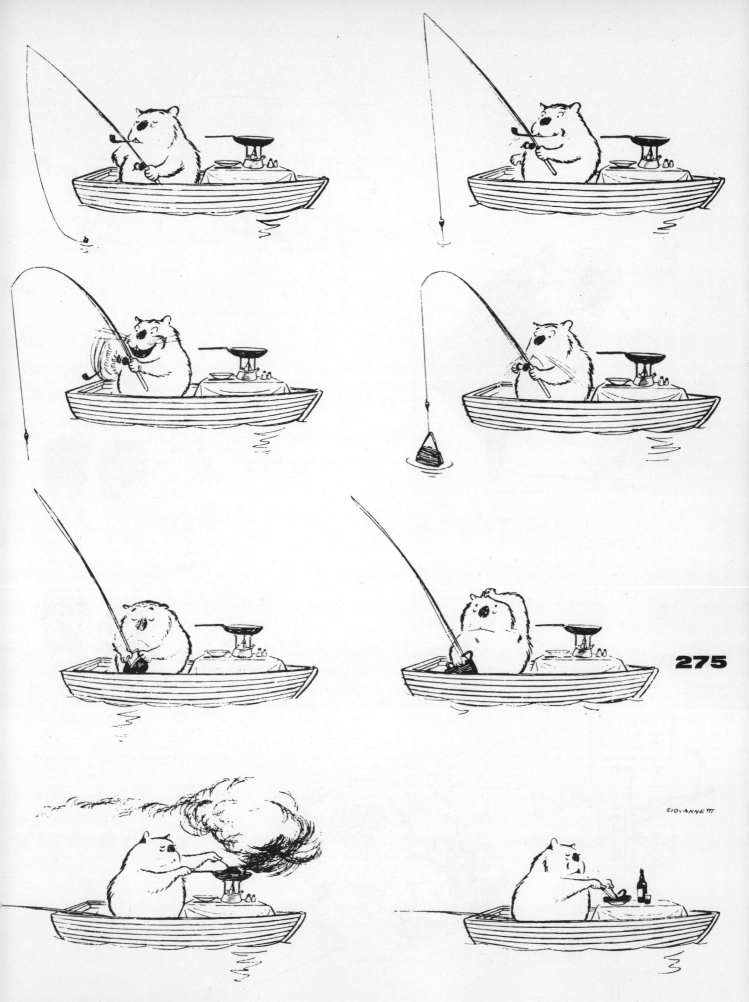

275

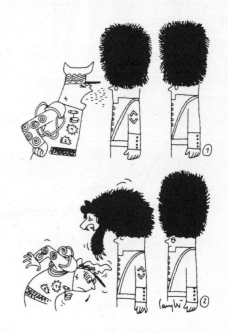

"You're deliberately paying attention just to confuse me."

BILL YATES, THE SATURDAY EVENING POST, U. S.

"Heavens! What cold hands you have!"

GUY BARA, SAMEDI-SOIR, FRANCE

CANZLER, NEUE ILLUSTRIERTE, GERMANY

276

VEHICLES
SLOW DOWN
TO 20 M.P.H.
OVER BRIDGE

EMILE MERCIER, SYDNEY SUN, AUSTRALIA

TREZ, MARIE FRANCE, FRANCE

277

"Is it for a gift?"

TETSU, FRANCE DIMANCHE, FRANCE

MOAL
LIC

"Kitchy-Koo!"

MOALIC, LA PRESSE, FRANCE

278

"Superstitious?"

NANDO, VIE NUOVE, ITALY

HOFFNUNG, NEUE ILLUSTRIERTE,
GERMANY

279

SPRING

DUBOUT, ICI PARIS, FRANCE

"*Darling, I swear to you, no woman has ever been here before.*"

SEMPÉ, SAMEDI-SOIR, FRANCE

280

EFFICIENT STATUE ADORNING TWO ROOMS AT A TIME

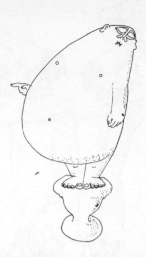

DISCREET STATUE TO GUIDE GUESTS

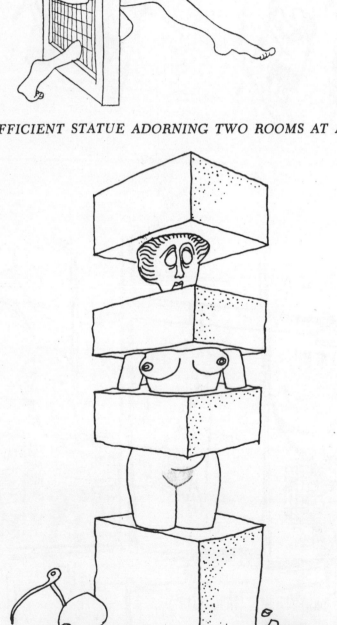

UNFINISHED STATUE SHOWING MORBID
INTEREST IN FEMALE ANATOMY

MULTI-PURPOSE STATUE FOR CIVIC PRIDE

GEORGE MOLNAR, ENGLAND

282

LAMB, ARGOSY, U. S.

JOE LANE, EXTENSION, U. S.

283

NASLUND, SE, SWEDEN

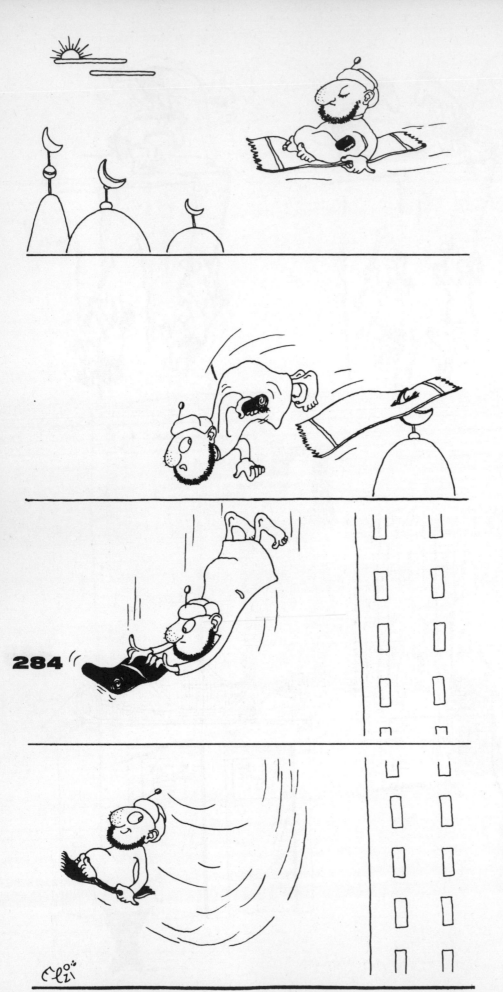

284

"Why don't you look where you're going?"

ERIC BURGIN, © PUNCH, ENGLAND

HANS ULRICH MEURY, DIE WOCHE,
SWITZERLAND

"Repeat: 33 . . . 33 . . ."

HERVÉ, FRANCE DIMANCHE, FRANCE

285

"How many times do I have to tell you to take off your gloves before you come in the house?"

MANZI, TEMPO, ITALY

"*Just a minute, I want to remove our fingerprints.*"

MORITZ, LUSTIGE ILLUSTRIERTE, GERMANY

"*He has a small but very devoted audience.*"

CISSIE PELTZ, CHICAGO TRIBUNE MAGAZINE OF BOOKS, U. S.

286

SAY IT WITH FLOWERS

DUBOUT, LE RIRE, FRANCE

MAHOOD, © PUNCH, ENGLAND

"Women and children first!"

RU, NOIR ET BLANC, FRANCE

287

"Eloise is the sweet uncomplaining type . . . I hate her."

CHON DAY, THE SATURDAY EVENING POST, U. S.

VÉTÉRINAIRE

288 herué

"It's difficult to take their temperatures."

HERVÉ, FRANCE DIMANCHE, FRANCE

"Something tells me he's going to try to steal home."

VIRGIL PARTCH, TRUE, U. S.

"Mother's not very intelligent, but I think you'll like her."

STEIG, LOOK, U. S.

290

HERVÉ, FRANCE DIMANCHE, FRANCE

291

BOSC

hervé

292

"He's very badly in debt so he's working overtime."

293

"I made your favorite dessert, and it was so delicious I ate it all up."

BILL YATES, THE SATURDAY EVENING POST, U. S.

294

MORITZ, LUSTIGE ILLUSTRIERTE, GERMANY

GEORGE BOOTH, COLLIER'S, U. S.

B. V. D. BORN, HET PAROOL, THE NETHERLANDS

295

THE MAN WHO APPLAUDED AT THE END OF THE FIRST MOVEMENT OF THE SYMPHONY

CHARLES E. KELLY, DUBLIN OPINION, IRELAND

"Toothpicks!"

ROLAND, MANCHETE, BRAZIL

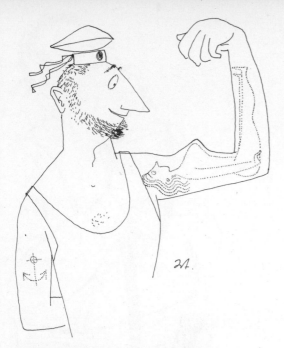

JULES STAUBER, DER STERN, GERMANY

297

RAYMOND PEYNET, FRANCE

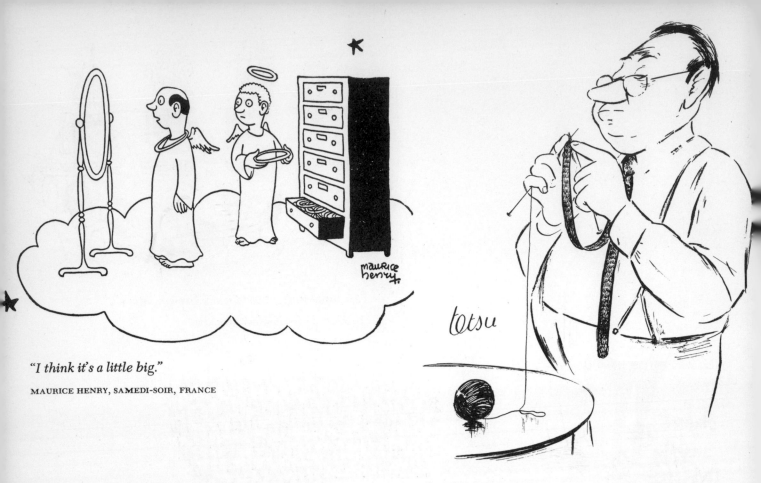

"I think it's a little big."

MAURICE HENRY, SAMEDI-SOIR, FRANCE

TETSU, ICI PARIS, FRANCE

298

"Don't worry Your Majesty, our pilot is an ace."

GRUM, ICI PARIS, FRANCE

299

"Doorbell. You answer it. I'm shaving."

JEAN BELLUS, FRANCE DIMANCHE, FRANCE

300

ISIDORI, IL TRAVASO, ITALY

LEON, DER STERN, GERMANY

301

CAVALLO, GAZZETTA SERA, ITALY

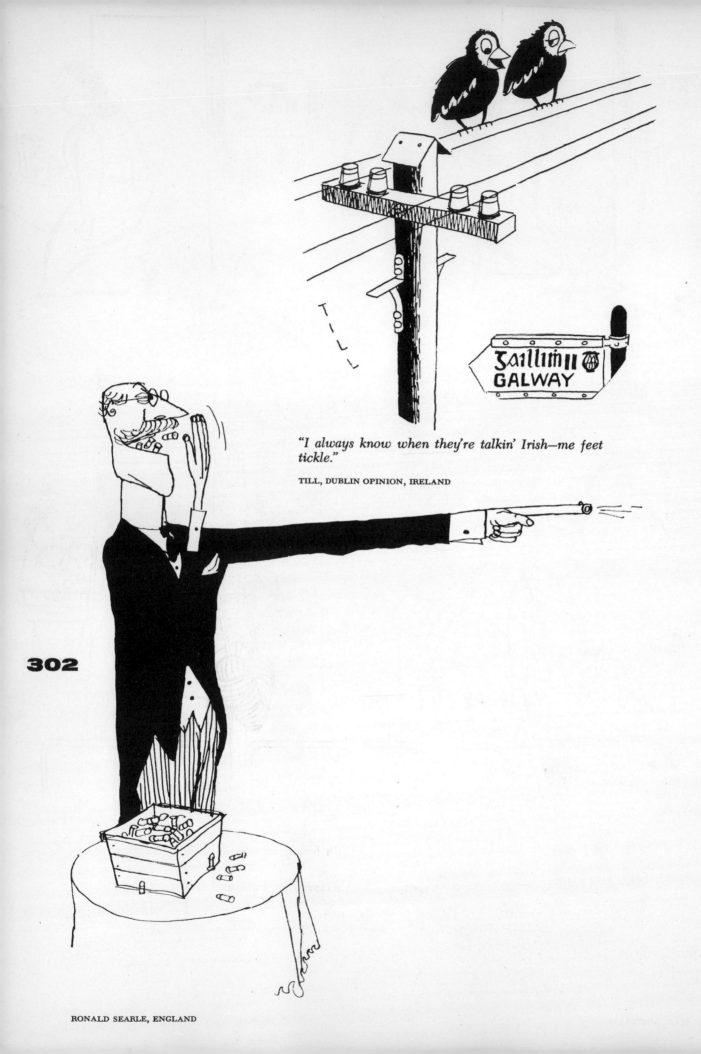

"*I always know when they're talkin' Irish—me feet tickle.*"

TILL, DUBLIN OPINION, IRELAND

302

RONALD SEARLE, ENGLAND

MALAYATOOR RAMAKRISHNAN, THE ILLUSTRATED WEEKLY OF INDIA, INDIA

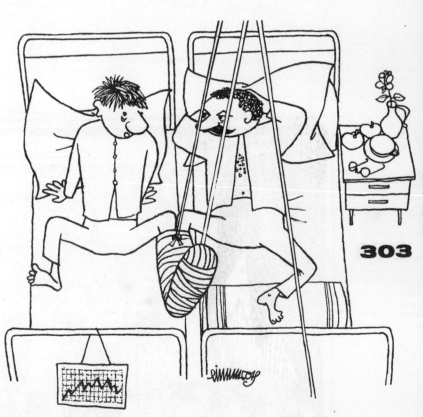

303

"*I guess we both belong to the same group hospitalization plan.*"

LIMMROTH, NEUE ILLUSTRIERTE, GERMANY

GIBSON, MAN, AUSTRALIA

THE GLADIATOR.

TED SCORFIELD, THE SYDNEY BULLETIN, AUSTRALIA

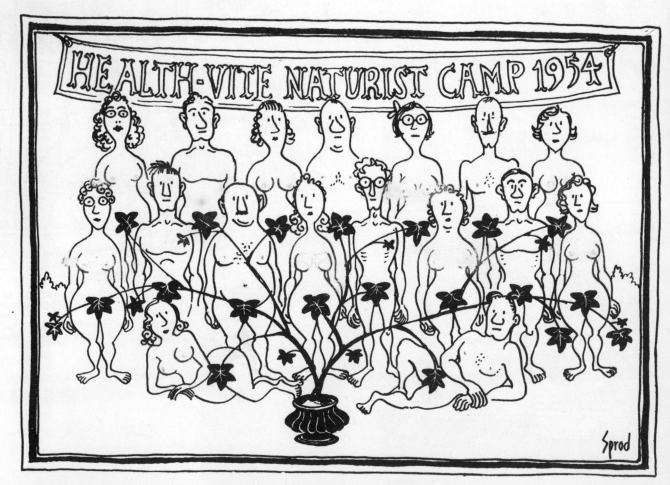

HEALTH-VITE NATURIST CAMP 1954

SPROD, © PUNCH, ENGLAND

Strauss (Johann)

Mozart

Beethoven

Wagner

Gershwin

Chopin (Valse triste)

Grieg

Tschaikowsky

305

Rossini

Rodriguez

Honegger

Finale

JÜRG SPAHR, NEBELSPALTER, SWITZERLAND

306

PETER NEUGEBAUER, GERMANY

HANS ULRICH MEURY, SIE UND ER, SWITZERLAND

LETTERS

CHAVAL, PARIS-MATCH, FRANCE

ERNST HEIDEMANN, GERMANY

"Here there was once a secret dungeon, the entrance to which has been lost."

DUBOUT, ICI PARIS, FRANCE

FOLCO, IL GIORNALE DELLA DOMENICA, ITALY

308

"I want my cards to say 'Travelers checks accepted' in French, English and German."

GANTRIIS, HUDIBRAS, DENMARK

SMILBY, MEN ONLY, ENGLAND

INDUCTION CENTER

LIMMROTH, FRANKFURTER ILLUSTRIERTE, GERMANY

309

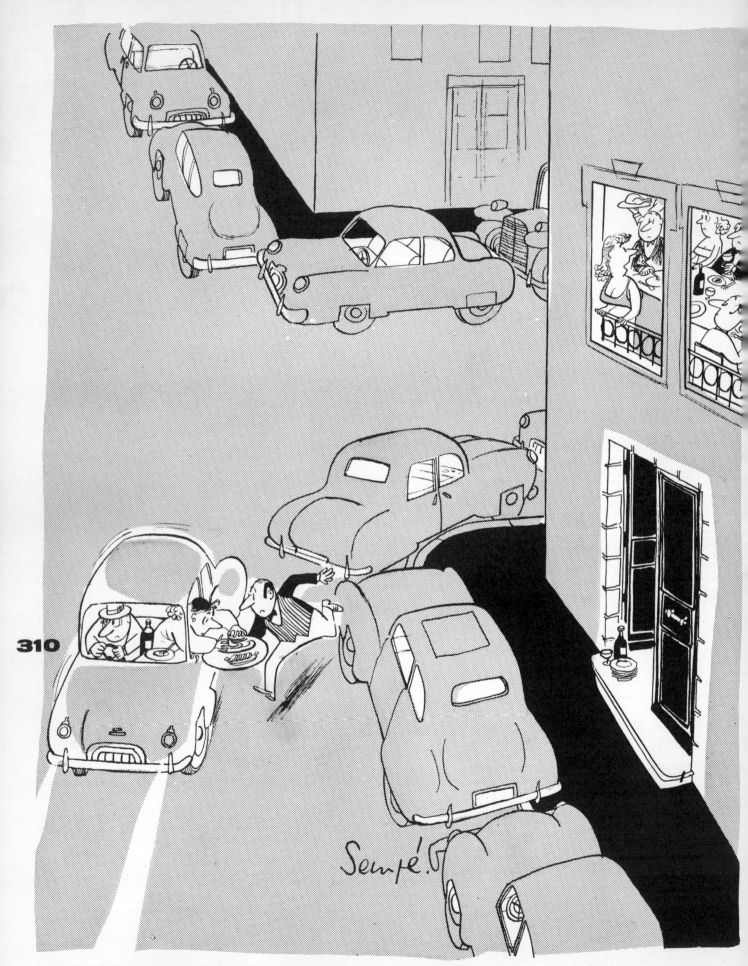

310

"*They still haven't found a parking place.*"

SEMPÉ, ICI PARIS, FRANCE

TREZ, SAMEDI-SOIR, FRANCE

"I'm going to repay you for all the glasses of water you got me when I was little. Want one now?"

LARRY REYNOLDS, LOOK, U. S.

311

CHAVAL, © PUNCH, ENGLAND

312

COSPER

"He's a man of few words."

COSPER, HUDIBRAS, DENMARK

FOLCO, IL TRAVASO, ITALY

FRANZ FÜCHSEL, HUDIBRAS, DENMARK

PETER GROSSKREUZ, REVUE, GERMANY

314

tetsu

TETSU, FRANCE DIMANCHE, FRANCE

"You're wasting your time, young man—I tell you we've already got one!"

GIBSON, MAN, AUSTRALIA

315

CHRISTINE KEMPTON, MARYLAND OLD LINE, U. S.

STARKE, © PUNCH, ENGLAND

316

"Help!"

CAVALLO, GAZZETTA SERA, ITALY

SOCIETY FOR THE PREVENTION OF CRUELTY TO ANIMALS

TREZ, PARIS-MATCH, FRANCE

DICK OUWEHAND, THE NETHERLANDS

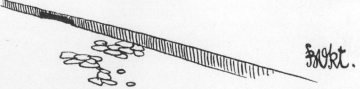

BORTOLATO, SETTIMO GIORNO, ITALY

317

PETER NEUGEBAUER, DER STERN, GERMANY

H. J. BRANDES, NEUE ILLUSTRIERTE, GERMANY

B. JEANSON, ICI PARIS, FRANCE

318

SEMPÉ, ICI PARIS, FRANCE

HOLBEK, HUDIBRAS, DENMARK

319

"Because of the indisposition of the lion, its place will be taken at tonight's performance by the tamer's wife."

MANZI, TEMPO, ITALY

CHAVAL, PARIS-MATCH, FRANCE

1700

1900

320

1950

BERTHAU, DER STERN, GERMANY

André François

ANDRÉ FRANÇOIS, FRANCE

86

KOVARSKY, PAGEANT, U.S.

"Do you serve minors?"

VIRGIL PARTCH, COLLIER'S, U.S.